Grammar *in use*
Intermediate
WORKBOOK
with answers

THIRD
EDITION

Present Continuous (I am doing)

Complete B's answers with the present continuous. Choose from the list.

begin to like	~~not get better~~	grow very fast	read the same one
improve all the time	make a salad	paint the bedrooms	take a shower
~~visit her~~	not snow	study law	not rise
not have a good time			

1. *A:* Why isn't Claire studying?

   B: Because some friends ___*are visiting her*___ .

2. *A:* Why is the doctor worried about your leg?

   B: It ___*isn't getting better*___ .

3. *A:* Why are you cutting tomatoes?

   B: Because I _____ .

4. *A:* Why are the Lee children sleeping in the living room?

   B: Because their parents _____ .

5. *A:* Why doesn't Bill answer his cell phone?

   B: He's in the bathroom. He _____ .

6. *A:* It's a nice party. Why do you want to go home?

   B: I _____ .

7. *A:* Is your sister in medical shool?

   B: No, she _____ .

8. *A:* Are you pleased with your English?

   B: Yes. It _____ .

9. *A:* You don't eat out much anymore.

   B: No, my salary _____ , but prices are.

10. *A:* Do you like the weather better now?

    B: Definitely. It _____ anymore.

11. *A:* How do you like your new job?

    B: Fine. I _____ my boss better now.

12. *A:* How is your new niece?

    B: Wonderful. She _____ .

13. *A:* What are Sheila and Sue talking about?

    B: A book. They _____

Simple Present (I do)

Complete B's responses to A. Use the simple present. Add necessary words. Two of B's responses are questions.

1. *A:* Do Mr. and Mrs. White ever use their balcony?

   B: Yes, _they eat dinner there_ (eat / dinner / there) when it's nice out.

2. *A:* Does Bob swim for exercise?

   B: No, _____ (usually / exercise) at the gym.

3. *A:* Where does Sarah do her homework?

   B: _____ (do / in the library) after school.

4. *A:* Who takes care of your little brother when your parents are at work?

   B: My grandma _____ (take care of / him) on weekdays.

5. *A:* Is Margaret a housewife?

   B: No, _____ (teach / math) in a high school.

6. *A:* Would you like a cup of coffee?

   B: No thanks. _____ (not / drink / coffee).

7. *A:* Why doesn't Amy talk to Ben?

   B: _____ (not / like / him) anymore.

8. *A:* Bill always gets to work early.

   B: I know. _____ (live) close to the office?

9. *A:* Why don't you want to talk to the boss?

   B: He _____ (not / look / very happy) this morning.

10. *A:* Are you and Maria having an argument again?

    B: Yes, _____ (never / agree) with me.

11. *A:* I'll buy you lunch if you help me clean my apartment.

    B: Really? _____ (promise)?

12. *A:* Hey, Bob. How about lending me some money to go to the movies?

    B: No, _____ (refuse / to give) you any more money. You didn't pay me back the last time.

13. *A:* Why is your boss so unpopular?

    B: _____ (not / apologize) when she's wrong.

14. *A:* Why are you mad at your son?

    B: _____ (not / do / anything / at home) to help me.

Present Continuous and Simple Present 1 (**I am doing** and **I do**)

On the next page, write sentences about the people in the pictures using the words in parentheses. Use the simple present or present continuous. Add necessary words.

Laura and Bob on a workday
Job: restaurant owners (10:00 a.m.–8:00 p.m., Tuesday–Sunday)

Laura and Bob today
Spare time: spending time with the children, playing tennis, hiking

EXERCISE CONTINUES ▶▶

1. (Laura and Bob / own / restaurant) *Laura and Bob own a restaurant.*

2. (they / not / work / today) *They aren't working today.*

3. (they / usually / work / 10 hours a day) _____

4. (Bob / cook / food / and Laura / serve / customers) _____

5. (Bob / not / cook / today) _____

6. (Laura / not / serve / customers / today) _____

7. (every day after school / the children / go / to the restaurant) _____

8. (they / usually / do / their homework / in the kitchen) _____

9. (they / not / do / homework / now) _____

10. (they / spend / time / with their parents / now) _____

11. (everyone / look / happy) _____

12. (sometimes / they / hike / in the hills / on Mondays) _____

13. (they / not / hike / this afternoon) _____

14. (today / they / play tennis together) _____

15. (Grandma / usually / visit / family / on Mondays) _____

16. (today / she / sit and watch / tennis game) _____

Present Continuous and Simple Present 2 (**I am doing** and **I do**)

Put the appropriate verb in the present continuous or the simple present.

1. (be, be)

   I don't know why Hannah is _being_ so difficult today. She _is_ usually very cooperative.*

2. (make, need)

   I _____ a salad for lunch today, but I _____ some tomatoes from the store.

3. (see, look)

   _____ you _____ the parking space over there?
   Or _____ you _____ for a bigger one?

4. (be, think)

   My friend Paul _____ very interesting. I _____ you'll like him.

5. (have, love, enjoy)

   A: (at a party) _____ you _____ a good time?
   B: Yes. I _____ parties. _____ you _____ yourself?

6. (always do, promise)

   A: Can we depend on Mike?
   B: Yes. He _____ what he _____ .

7. (begin, always ask)

   I _____ to get tired of Sylvia. She _____ me the same questions about my family.

8. (think, like)

   My sister _____ of applying to medical school because she _____ chemistry and biology.

9. (mean, depend, have)

   A: What _____ this word _____ ?
   B: It _____ . It _____ lots of meanings.

10. (belong, contain)

    This salad _____ in the refrigerator because it _____ eggs.

11. (not realize, be)

    What's wrong with you? You _____ how childish you _____ right now.

12. (use, eat)

    A: (at a coffee shop) _____ you _____ this chair, or can I take it?
    B: Help yourself. I _____ alone.

*cooperative: *willing to do what somebody needs or asks; working well with others*

Simple Past (**I did**)

Use the words in parentheses to write sentences in the simple past. Some are questions.

1. (we / go / for a walk / in the park / last night)
   We went for a walk in the park last night.

2. (you / do / your exercises / this morning?)
   Did you do your exercises this morning?

3. (I / not / have / time / to visit my parents / last night) _____
   _____

4. (you / see / the sunset / last night?) _____

5. (the baby / not / eat / all her breakfast / this morning) _____
   _____

6. (you / be / on time for work / yesterday?) _____

7. (my friends / not / get / a good price / for their house / last month) _____
   _____

8. (you / spend / too much money / on your last haircut) _____
   _____

9. (Amy / lose / her ring, / but / I / find / it / yesterday) _____
   _____

10. (anyone / get hurt / in the accident / yesterday morning?) _____
    _____

11. (you / be / happy / to see Claudia again / last week?) _____
    _____

12. (we / not / have / enough money / to get / tickets / for last night's concert) _____
    _____

13. (how / Ann / catch / a cold?) _____

14. (you / forget / our teacher's name / again?) _____

15. (Sam / not / do / anything wrong) _____

16. (the book / cost / a lot, / but / I / buy / it / anyway) _____
    _____

17. (Rose / go / to that restaurant / three times / and / order / the same thing) _____
    _____

Simple Present (I do); Present Continuous (I'm doing); Simple Past (I did)

Complete the dialogs with the verbs in the boxes. Use the present (simple or continuous) or the simple past for each verb. Some sentences are questions.

be	change	enjoy	have	not go

1. *A:* _Did_ you _enjoy_ the new Indonesian restaurant last night?

    B: Well, we _changed_ our minds and _didn't go_ there.

    A: Where _did_ you _have_ dinner then?

    B: At home. I _'m (OR am)_ a very good cook, you know.

be	look	rain	not rain	snow

2. *A:* *(on the phone)* Did you get rain last night?

    B: It _____ a little in the next town, but it _____ at all here.
    How _____ the weather there today?

    A: Actually, it _____ right now. It _____ beautiful.
    B: Unbelievable!

go	read	want

3. *A:* Are you busy?

    B: No. I _____ an e-mail from a friend. Why?

    A: I _____ to lunch. _____ you _____ to come with me?
    B: Sure, if you can wait a minute.

take	visit

4. *A:* Where's Emily tonight?

    B: I suppose she _____ her uncle in the hospital. They _____ him there in an ambulance last night.

not be	study

5. *A:* Is Ben meeting us at the movies?

    B: He can't. He _____ for a test tomorrow, so he _____ free tonight.

go	not see	take care of

6. *A:* _____ Janine _____ to the meeting last night?

    B: Probably not. She _____ her niece this week.

    A: That explains why I _____ her there.

happen	have

7. *A:* Why are you so late? _____ something _____ ?

    B: Sorry. I _____ a flat tire on the way here.

Past Continuous (**I was doing**)

Complete B's responses using the past continuous. Use the simple past of the verb in parentheses for the second part of your sentence.

1. *A:* My brother is studying law now. (see)

   B: Really? *He wasn't studying law the last time I saw him.*

2. *A:* I'm working for a computer company now. (talk to)

   B: Really? *You weren't working for a computer company the last time I talked to you.*

3. *A:* I know the president of my company now. (speak)

   B: Really? *You didn't know him (her) the last time I spoke to you.*

4. *A:* The Johnsons are taking a cooking class. (see)

   B: Really? _____

5. *A:* My brother exercises a lot now. (talk to)

   B: Really? _____

6. *A:* I want to change jobs. (see)

   B: Really? _____

7. *A:* Carol makes commercials* for TV. (talk to)

   B: Really? _____

8. *A:* George is having trouble at work. (speak)

   B: Really? _____

9. *A:* We're talking about adopting* a baby. (talk to)

   B: Really? _____

10. *A:* I work at home two days a week now. (see)

    B: Really? _____

11. *A:* Brad and his wife are having problems. (speak)

    B: Really? _____

12. *A:* We are thinking of moving to Toronto. (talk to)

    B: Really? _____

13. *A:* I know a lot of people in the city now. (talk to)

    B: Really? _____

14. *A:* Carl is trying to lose weight. (speak)

    B: Really? _____

*commercial: *a paid advertisement on TV or radio*   *adopt: *to accept someone else's child into a family through a legal process*

Simple Past (**I did**); Past Continuous (**I was doing**)

Look at the illustration of an accident. Then complete the passage. Put the verbs in the simple past or the past continuous.

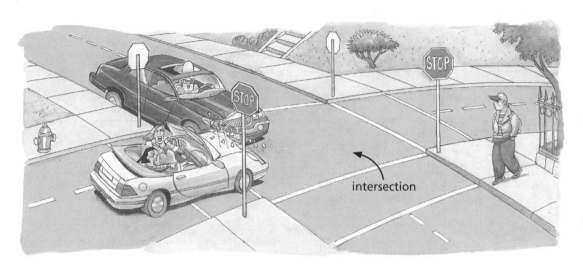

intersection

I **1)** ___saw___ (see) an accident while I **2)** ___was walking___ (walk) to work this morning. The accident, between a blue car and a white car, **3)** _____ (happen) because the driver of the white car **4)** _____ (not / see) the stop sign. The driver of the blue car **5)** _____ (slow) down and **6)** _____ (stop) at the sign at her corner. The driver of the white car **7)** _____ (not / notice) the stop sign because she **8)** _____ (talk) to a passenger in her car. For some reason, the passenger **9)** _____ (sit) in the back seat, and the driver **10)** _____ (turn) around once or twice to look at her.

The white car **11)** _____ (drive) into the intersection while the blue car **12)** _____ (cross) it. The driver of the white car **13)** _____ (try) to stop, but it **14)** _____ (be) too late. She **15)** _____ (hit) the front of the blue car. Fortunately, no one was hurt, probably because at the moment of the crash, both cars **16)** _____ (move) slowly. After the accident, the drivers of both cars **17)** _____ (get out) and **18)** _____ (check) their vehicles.* They **19)** _____ (speak) to each other briefly to make sure that no one **20)** _____ (have) a serious injury. Five minutes later, the police **21)** _____ (arrive) and **22)** _____ (make) an accident report. Although it all **23)** _____ (happen) very quickly, I **24)** _____ still _____ (think) about it when I got to work.

*vehicles: *cars, buses, and trucks*

Present and Past

XERCISE
9

UNITS
1–6

Read B's answer, and then write A's question. Use words from the box with a question word (*What, Why, Where, When, Who,* or *How*). Use the present or past tense (simple or continuous).

your glasses / be	you / be / so nervous	you / do / at 10:00 last night
~~you / go / on vacation~~	~~you / go / to bed~~	you / leave / the house
we / need / from the store		

1. *A:* _Why are you going to bed_ so early?
   B: Because I have to get up at 4:00 a.m. tomorrow morning.

2. *A:* _Where did you go on vacation_ last summer?
   B: To Colorado.

3. *A:* _____ this morning?
   B: At 7:30. I had an early meeting at work.

4. *A:* _____
   B: Watching TV. Why?

5. *A:* _____
   B: Just bread and milk today. I got everything else yesterday.

6. *A:* _____
   B: Because I'm going to the dentist today, and I'm scared.

7. *A:* _____
   B: I found them in the car.

you / be / so difficult today	the mail carrier* / come
you / find / my keys	the thieves / get / into the school
you / talk / to / on the phone	

8. *A:* _____
   B: Usually around 2:00 p.m.

9. *A:* _____
   B: They were in the drawer in the kitchen.

10. *A:* _____
    B: It's Mom. Do you want to talk to her?

11. *A:* _____
    B: Sorry. I have a headache, so I'm in a bad mood.

12. *A:* _____
    B: The back door was open.

*mail carrier: *person who delivers mail (letters, postcards, packages) to a home or business*

11

Present and Past

Complete the sentences with your own ideas.

1. Sometimes I get <u>*hungry*</u> when <u>*I am thinking hard in class*</u> .
    Sometimes I get <u>*angry with myself*</u> when <u>*I make mistakes*</u> .
    Sometimes I get <u>*to class late*</u> when <u>*my children are sick*</u> .
    Sometimes I get _____ when _____ .

2. The people who live next to me are _____
    _____ in their yard right now.

3. Last month two interesting things happened: **1)** _____
    _____ , and **2)** _____ .

4. One time, I hurt my _____ while I was
    _____ .

5. My family says that I am always _____ .

6. Sometimes people say that I look _____
    when I actually feel _____ .

7. I am thinking about _____ next year.

8. I understand why _____ , but I don't believe
    _____ .

9. I was _____ , but my friend
    wanted to _____ .

10. I think that people _____ .

11. At 10:30 a.m. yesterday, my friends _____
    _____ .

12. A long time ago when I was _____ , I found
    _____ .

13. Last year I _____ , but this year
    _____ .

14. When the sun rose yesterday, I _____
    _____ .

Present Perfect

Complete B's answers. Use the present perfect of the verb in parentheses. Some answers are negative. Some are questions. Use *ever* and *never* where possible.

1. *A:* Is Paris nice?

   B: Yes, it's the most beautiful city ___I've ever seen_____ (see).

2. *A:* Is Montreal a nice city to visit?

   B: Absolutely. ___I've been_____ (be) there many times.

3. *A:* Would you like to go skating with us some time?

   B: I don't know. ___I've never gone_____ (go) skating before.

4. *A:* Is it true that you got another raise?

   B: Yes. It's the second time _____ (get) one this year.

5. *A:* I'm sure you'll like Japan.

   B: Really? _____ (be) there?

6. *A:* Do you and your roommate go to the movies much?

   B: Yes, _____ (go) twice this week already.

7. *A:* It isn't that hard to ride a camel.

   B: Is that so? _____ (ride) a camel?

8. *A:* Do you play a lot of basketball?

   B: No, this is the first time _____ (play).

9. *A:* Where are my keys?

   B: I don't know. _____ (see) them today.

10. *A:* Are you excited that your grandfather is coming to see you?

    B: Yes. _____ (not / come) for two years.

11. *A:* Try not to feel too bad about failing the physics test.

    B: Easy for you to say. _____ (fail) a test?

12. *A:* Is it hard to write a poem?

    B: I don't know. _____ (write) one.

13. *A:* Is that salad good?

    B: I don't know. _____ (try) it yet.

14. *A:* Do you recommend this book?

    B: Well, it's good, but it's one of the longest books I _____ (read).

15. *A:* Tim can't find his wallet again.

    B: You're kidding.* That's the third time _____ (lose) it this year.

*You're kidding: *You're not serious.*

Are the underlined parts of these sentences right or wrong? Correct them where necessary.

1. Where <u>have you put</u> my wallet?   _RIGHT_

2. I<u>'ve lost</u> weight, but I gained it back again.   _I lost_

3. I don't know what Kim looks like yet.
   I <u>didn't see</u> him.   _____

4. They <u>have had</u> a tree in the front yard, but they
   cut it down.   _____

5. Your brother and his wife <u>just left</u>.   _____

6. The cost of gas <u>has gone up</u>, but it's going
   down again.   _____

7. I<u>'ve already done</u> my homework.   _____

8. I felt good at work all day because I<u>'ve eaten</u>
   a good breakfast.   _____

9. <u>Did you eat</u> lunch yet?   _____

10. <u>Have you seen</u> any good movies recently?   _____

11. My grandfather <u>has grown up</u> in France.   _____

12. Christine is a well-known architect. She
    <u>designed</u> many big buildings.   _____

13. Mike is a good college student, but he
    <u>has had</u> problems in high school.   _____

14. Oh no! You<u>'ve cut</u> my hair too short.   _____

15. I<u>'ve had</u> a backache earlier today, but I feel
    fine now.   _____

16. The Egyptians <u>have built</u> the first pyramids.   _____

17. Mark has just gotten back home. He <u>spent</u> six
    months on a project in Korea.   _____

18. I <u>haven't remembered</u> your brother's birthday,
    but I have a present for him now.   _____

19. He got a good grade on his report because
    he <u>has written</u> it very carefully.   _____

20. I know this computer works. I<u>'ve used</u> it.   _____

Present Perfect and Simple Past

Complete the sentences. Use the present perfect or simple past. Some answers are negative.

1. Sally swam a lot last year, but _she hasn't swum_____ much this year.

2. It hasn't rained so far this week, but _it rained_____ a lot last week.

3. My parents have been to Mexico, but _they haven't been_____ to Puerto Rico.

4. We took a long vacation in 2007, but _____ one since then.

5. Many people went to shelters* before the flood came, but very few _____ _____ to shelters in the last few days.

6. I didn't know Max in high school, but _____ him for the past 20 years.

7. I paid all the bills last month, but _____ any so far this month.

8. My car hasn't broken down recently, but _____ twice last month.

9. I know how to drive a car, but _____ a truck before.

10. I ate a big dinner last night, but _____ anything since then.

11. My father grew up in Chicago, but my mother _____ there. She's from Michigan.

12. Oil companies made big profits last week; actually, _____ big profits all this year.

13. Two friends of mine just got married, but _____ married in a church. The wedding was at the beach.

14. This is the first time I've ridden a horse, but _____ a bike when I was little.

15. The police arrested two people on the night of the robbery, but _____ anyone since that night.

16. I think I've met your sister, but _____ your brothers.

17. Sue hasn't been late for work once this week, but _____ late a lot this year.

18. It was really hot last month, but _____ cool recently.

19. We ate out a lot last year, but we _____ much this year.

20. I haven't seen your family in years, but I _____ photos of many of them at your sister's wedding a while ago.

*shelter: *building designed to give protection from bad weather*

15

Present Perfect and Past

Present Perfect Continuous (I have been doing)

Complete A's question or B's answer. Use the words in parentheses and any other necessary words. Use the present perfect continuous.

1. *A:* (Mike / live / with his parents) _Has Mike been living with his parents_ ?
    B: No, he got his own place as soon as he moved back here.

2. *A:* Is your sister still working at IBM?
    B: (work there) Yes, _she's been working there_ for six years.

3. *A:* *(in a car)* Are you tired of driving yet? Do you want me to drive?
    B: (drive / for three hours) Yes, I _____ .

4. *A:* (you / watch / TV all night) _____ ?
    B: No, we did our homework first.

5. *A:* Have you done anything interesting recently?
    B: (take / dance lessons) Yes, _____ for three weeks now.

6. *A:* (how long / you and Sam / stay / in a hotel) _____
    _____ ?
    B: Since we got here two weeks ago.

7. *A:* (you / do / exercises / for a long time) _____
    _____ ?
    B: No, I just started.

8. *A:* How is Ben doing these days?
    B: (spend / a lot of time) Fine, I think. He _____
    with his family.

9. *A:* Are you trying to lose weight?
    B: (exercise / and / eat less) Yes, _____
    _____ for a month now.

10. *A:* (how long / Sue / work / in Australia) _____
    _____ ?
    B: Since she left her old job last August.

11. *A:* Clare and Pat have wet hair – how strange.
    B: (swim) Yes, they _____ .

Present Perfect Continuous and Simple (**I have been doing** and **I have done**)

Write a question using the first group of words in parentheses. Use the present perfect simple or continuous. Then write an answer using the second group of words.

1. *A:* (how long / you / work / on your car?)

   How long have you been working on your car?

   B: (I / work / for almost two hours)

   I've been working for almost two hours.

2. *A:* (how many letters / Mark / finish?)

   How many letters has Mark finished?

   B: (he / write / six letters so far)

   _____

3. *A:* (how long / you / do / your homework?)

   _____

   B: (I / study / since breakfast)

   _____

4. *A:* (how much money / Sonia / spend / today?)

   _____

   B: (she / spend / $300 already)

   _____

5. *A:* (how long / Joe and Ina / dance?)

   _____

   B: (they / dance / all evening)

   _____

6. *A:* (how many times / you / play cards / this week?)

   _____

   B: (I / play / three times)

   _____

7. *A:* (how many rooms / he / paint / today?)

   _____

   B: (he / finish / three rooms)

   _____

Present Perfect Continuous and Simple (**I have been doing** and **I have done**); **How long have you (been)** . . . ?

Complete the dialogs with the words in parentheses. Use the present perfect continuous if possible; otherwise, use the present perfect simple.

1. *A:* How long *have you been swimming* _____ (you / swim)?
   B: About a half hour, I guess.

2. *A:* What's wrong with this door?
   B: *Someone has broken* _____ (someone / break) the lock.

3. *A:* How many flowers _____ (you / deliver) this morning?
   B: I've taken flowers to 12 homes and businesses.

4. *A:* Do you still eat at that Chinese restaurant?
   B: No, _____ (we / not / eat) there for a long time.

5. *A:* How long _____ (you / work) as a computer salesman?
   B: Since 2001.

6. *A:* _____ always _____ (your wife / work)?
   B: Yes, ever since we got married.

7. *A:* Do you think Stan is telling the truth?
   B: Yes, I do. _____ never _____ (he / tell) me a lie.

8. *A:* How long _____ (your father / sell) cars?
   B: For five or six years.

9. *A:* Isn't Julie amazing?
   B: Yes, _____ never _____ (I / know) anyone like her.

10. *A:* How long _____ (your sister / try) to get a job?
    B: Since she finished college six months ago.

11. *A:* Did your brother and his wife just get married?
    B: No, _____ (they / be) married for ages.

12. *A:* Shall we rent a DVD to watch?
    B: Great idea. _____ (I / not / see) a movie in ages.

13. *A:* How many parking tickets* _____ (you / get) since you started driving?
    B: Only two.

14. *A:* Are Stan and Sue still at the park?
    B: Yes, _____ (they / play) tennis for two hours.

parking ticket: a note saying you have to pay money for parking in the wrong place

Present Perfect and Past

Which sentences follow logically from the first one? Check (✓) one or two sentences.

1. Megan is 13 and knows how to ride a bicycle.
    ✓ a. She's ridden a bicycle before.
    ____ b. She has known how to ride a bike for a long time.
    ____ c. She's been riding her bike after school this week.
    ✓ d. She learned to ride a bike when she was younger.
    ____ e. She has had a bike for a long time.

2. Mr. Smith has been in the hospital since last week.
    ____ a. He has had an operation.
    ____ b. He went to the hospital last week.
    ____ c. He is in the hospital now.
    ____ d. He has been in the hospital several times.
    ____ e. This is the first time he's been in the hospital.

3. Sylvia and Glen have been married to each other for 17 years.
    ____ a. They are one of the happiest couples I've met.
    ____ b. They have known each other for a long time.
    ____ c. They knew each other for a long time before they got married.
    ____ d. They got married 17 years ago.
    ____ e. Neither Sylvia nor Glen was married before.

4. Sam just won $5,000 in the lottery.
    ____ a. He has been buying lottery tickets for a long time.
    ____ b. That is the first time he's bought a lottery ticket.
    ____ c. He has bought at least one lottery ticket in his life.
    ____ d. He has never won the lottery before.
    ____ e. Today, he is $5,000 richer than he was last week.

5. This is the third time our teacher has given us a quiz this month.
    ____ a. We've had three quizzes so far this month.
    ____ b. We haven't had a quiz for a long time.
    ____ c. The teacher has been giving a lot of quizzes recently.
    ____ d. The teacher didn't give us a quiz before this one.
    ____ e. This was the hardest quiz we've had all semester.

6. Sally has been to Japan twice.
    ____ a. She has gone to Japan recently.
    ____ b. She's in Japan now.
    ____ c. Sally has lived in Japan.
    ____ d. She has never been to Korea.
    ____ e. Sally has taken two trips to Japan.

Present Perfect and Past

How long have you (been) . . . ?; For and since; When . . . ? and How long . . . ?

A. Complete B's answer. Use the words in parentheses with *for*, *since*, or *ago*.

1. *A:* How long have you been using the computer?

    B: I've been using it _for two hours_ (two hours).

2. *A:* When did you get your invitation to Jack's wedding?

    B: I got it _a long time ago_ (a long time).

3. *A:* Are you still on a diet?

    B: Yes, I've been on one _____ (I went to the doctor's).

4. *A:* Do you go to the movies very often?

    B: No, we haven't been to the movies _____ (ages).

5. *A:* Is your sister still a nurse?

    B: Yes, she's been a nurse _____ (the year before last).

6. *A:* How long has it been since you bought a new TV?

    B: I haven't bought one _____ (about 10 years).

7. *A:* When did the Smiths buy their house?

    B: They bought it _____ (two or three years).

B. Complete A's questions. Use the words in parentheses. Use *How long* + present perfect (simple or continuous) or *When* + simple past.

1. *A:* _How long have you lived / been living here_ (you / live / here)?

    B: Since last April.

2. *A:* _____ (you / be / sick)?

    B: For almost a week now.

3. *A:* _____ (you / get / sick)?

    B: Last Friday at work.

4. *A:* _____ (your brother / travel / in Asia)?

    B: For six months so far.

5. *A:* _____ (it / be / since you got this job)?

    B: About two months now.

6. *A:* _____ (you / get / glasses)?

    B: After my appointment with the eye doctor last month.

Past Perfect (**I had done**)

Read the first sentence. Write two more sentences about it using the words in parentheses. Use the simple past in one sentence and the past perfect in the other.

1. Ana was very happy when we visited her last night.
   (her son / call / her from Argentina) *Her son had called her from Argentina.*
   (she / tell / us about his new job) *She told us about his new job.*

2. Someone broke into* the Smiths' house yesterday.
   (they / not / be / home at the time) *They weren't (were not) home at the time.*
   (they / leave / a window open) *They had left a window open.*

3. I was getting off the train yesterday when I saw an old friend.
   (she / be / away for several years) _____
   (we / have / a long talk) _____

4. I was very tired last night.
   (I / work / very hard all day) _____
   (I / not / brush / my teeth before bed) _____
   _____

5. Sam and Amy finally got married last year.
   (everyone / be / happy for them) _____
   (they / know / each other for seven years) _____

6. Jim changed a flat tire on his car yesterday.
   (it / be / difficult for him) _____
   (he / never / do / it before) _____

7. Someone rang Linda's doorbell late last night.
   (Linda / go to bed / early) _____
   (the doorbell / not / wake / her) _____

8. An old friend called me last night.
   (we / not / talk / to each other for ages) _____
   (we / spend / an hour / talking about old times) _____

9. Mike and I stopped at a café after the movie last night.
   (Mike / eat / something / before the movie) _____
   (he / not / order / anything) _____

*break into: *to enter a building in order to steal something*

Past Perfect Continuous (**I had been doing**) and Past Continuous (**I was doing**)

Write B's answers with the words in parentheses and other necessary words. Use the past perfect continuous or the past continuous.

A	**B**
1. Why was Phil angry at us when we met him yesterday?	(wait / a long time) _He'd been waiting a long time_ .
2. Did Sarah see the accident?	(look / in shop windows) _No, she was looking in shop windows_ .
3. Why was Roger upset when he got to work?	(sit / in traffic for two hours) _____ _____ .
4. Didn't you ask Susan to come to the movies with us?	(study / for a test) Yes, but _____ _____ .
5. Why didn't Stan and his wife speak to each other at dinner last night?	(have / an argument) It seems _____ _____ about something.
6. Why didn't Freddie answer the phone? Wasn't he home?	(water / flowers in the garden) Yes, but _____ _____ when the phone rang.
7. Why was Jennifer so tired last night?	(swim / all afternoon) _____ _____ .
8. Why didn't you say hello when I passed you on the sidewalk this morning?	(talk / on my cell phone) Sorry. _____ _____ .
9. Is your sister happy that she had a baby boy?	(hope / for a girl) Of course, but _____ _____ .
10. Why did that supermarket close down?	(lose money / for months) They _____ _____ .
11. How did you get so wet?	(rain / hard / a minute ago) Well, _____ _____ .
12. Were you surprised when Sam lost his job?	(expect it / for months) Not really, I _____ _____ .
13. The Smiths were very glad to get back home last week.	(travel / abroad / for three months) That's understandable. They _____ _____ .

Present Perfect and Past Perfect

Write a second sentence with an idea from the box. Use the present perfect or past perfect, simple or continuous.

> buy tickets for years
> look at a computer screen for hours
> not feel well since lunchtime
> ~~spend two weeks there~~
>
> have a good time here
> not eat anything all day
> ~~not sleep well recently~~

1. Kate has been yawning all morning.

   She _hasn't been sleeping well recently_ .

2. Mark and Raul showed us pictures of their trip to Peru when we saw them last night.

   They _had spent two weeks there_ .

3. I was really surprised when I won the lottery last month.

   I _____ .

4. I don't feel like going to the movies tonight.

   I _____ .

5. No wonder* Reuben had such a healthy appetite at dinner last night.

   He _____ .

6. No wonder your eyes are so sore.*

   You _____ .

7. We are glad we came to Hawaii for vacation.

   We _____ .

> ask for something sweet
> give her an injection
>
> never be there before
> want to see it for a long time

8. I finally saw that Hungarian movie you told me about.

   I _____ .

9. Magdalena is excited about her trip to Guatemala.

   She _____ .

10. Jenny was very relaxed when the dentist pulled her tooth.

    He _____ .

11. Do we have any cookies for the children?

    They _____ .

*No wonder: *I am not surprised*   *sore: *painful and uncomfortable*

Past, Present Perfect, and Past Perfect

Look at the picture and complete the story using the words in parentheses. Use the simple or continuous form of the past, present perfect, or past perfect. Put the verb in the correct form. Add other necessary words.

1. a. Sam _woke up_____ (wake up) in the middle of the night a few days ago.

    b. He _had been sleeping_____ (sleep) very soundly.*

    c. His little boy _was crying_____ (cry) in the next room.

    d. Sam _____ (go / to see) what was wrong.

    e. Mikey _____ (stop / crying) when he saw his father.

    f. He _____ (have) a bad dream.

    g. Mikey _____ (not / wake up) at night since then.

    h. Both Sam and his son _____ (sleep) very well since then.

2. a. I _____ (swim) at an outdoor* pool two weeks ago at about 3:00 p.m.

    b. I _____ (have) a good time and _____ (enjoy) the cool water.

    c. It was the first time I _____ (swim) all summer.

    d. Suddenly, there _____ (be) a flash of lightning* in the sky.

    e. The lifeguard* _____ (tell) us to get out of the pool.

    f. I _____ (be) a little angry about that.

    g. I _____ (pay) two dollars to swim, but I _____ (be) in the pool for only five minutes.

    h. I _____ (not / go) back to that pool since that day.

*soundly: *deeply and peacefully*   *outdoor: *not in a building*   *flash of lightning: *bright light in the sky during a storm*   *lifeguard: *person who watches swimmers and helps them when they are in trouble*

Used to (do) and Past Continuous (I was doing)

Complete B's responses using phrases from the box. Add other necessary words. Use the past continuous (*was doing*) or *used to* (*do*).

~~be very cheap~~	have a nice big one	have trouble with her car
not pay attention	run and play basketball	take a nap*
~~talk on the phone~~		

1. *A:* Did you give the boss my message this morning?

   B: No, _she was talking on the phone_ . I wasn't able to speak to her.

2. *A:* Do you think gas has gotten expensive?

   B: Yes, I do. _It used to be very cheap._

3. *A:* Do you have a tent I can borrow to go camping?

   B: No, sorry, _____ , but I lost it.

4. *A:* Did Susan meet you and Sam for coffee yesterday?

   B: No, _____ . It wouldn't start.

5. *A:* Do you try to get some exercise every day?

   B: I just walk now, but _____ .

6. *A:* Why didn't you answer the phone? I called three times.

   B: Sorry, my cell phone was turned off. _____ .

7. *A:* How did the accident happen?

   B: A driver was talking on a cell phone and _____ .

not celebrate it	celebrate their victory*
pay attention	work on a project

8. *A:* *(to teacher)* Why have my son's grades* gone down?

   B: He's been talking to his friends a lot in class. _____ , but now he doesn't.

9. *A:* Do you celebrate your birthday in some way?

   B: _____ , but now I have a party every year.

10. *A:* Why did the basketball team get to bed so late last night?

    B: They _____ .

11. *A:* We waited two hours for you last night. Why didn't you come to the party?

    B: Sorry. _____ but didn't finish it.

*take a nap: *to sleep for a short time, usually during the day*   *victory: *success*   *grades: *points or letter mark (A, B, C) given by a teacher for a student's work in school*

Past, Present Perfect, and Past Perfect

Read the passage about a tennis match between two friends.

I had an experience that taught me something yesterday. My friend Paul won our tennis match yesterday morning. I felt tired halfway through the match because I hadn't had a very good breakfast and hadn't slept well the night before. An old couple at the park was having a little argument while they watched us play. The man wanted to give me advice on my tennis game, but his wife stopped him from saying anything. I was embarrassed that the man was watching. Also, I was disappointed in how badly I played, because I used to beat Paul at tennis all the time. He was nice about it, though. He didn't brag* about winning the match. I had something to eat and rested after the match. I felt much better then. I have learned that practice, food, and sleep are important. Paul and I have got another match next week. I have decided to practice a lot before then, to have a good breakfast every morning, and to get enough sleep every night.

Write a similar paragraph about an experience that taught you something. Use these questions as a guide:

1. What happened?
2. What did you learn from the experience?
3. How has it changed you?

Use the space below to make a brief outline. Then write your composition on a separate piece of paper.

_____

*brag: *to speak with pride, often too proudly, about something you have done*

Present Tenses (**I am doing / I do**) with a Future Meaning

Complete the dialog between a personal assistant (A) and her boss (B). Use the words in parentheses. Use the present continuous or simple present.

A: I came in early this morning so that I can leave work early tonight. Trains to my town
1) _don't run_ (not / run) after 6:00 p.m. But I wanted to get here early to arrange things
for today, so I left home at 7:00 a.m.

B: Thank you for that. So, what **2)** _am I doing_ (I / do) this morning? Have you arranged
everything?

A: Yes. In 15 minutes, **3)** _____ (you / meet) with a group of salesmen to talk
about new products. After that, **4)** _____ (you / call) your travel agent about
vacation plans. At 10:30, **5)** _____ (the director / come) to your office for a
half-hour meeting with you. Then **6)** _____ (a writer / help) you prepare
your speech for the company dinner tonight. **7)** _____ (I / not / type) it until
you finish. According to the schedule, **8)** _____ (the dinner / begin) at 7:00,
9) _____ (you / speak) from 8:00 to 8:15, and **10)** _____
(the dinner / not / end) until 9:00. Any questions so far?

B: Yes, are you sure you've arranged everything? **11)** _____ (I / get) a haircut
before the dinner? **12)** _____ (you / pick up) my suit from the dry cleaner?
13) _____ (who / order) flowers for the guest table?

A: **14)** _____ (you / not / get) a haircut until after lunch. I've already ordered
the flowers, and **15)** _____ (I / pick up) your suit after work.
16) _____ (the dry cleaner / close) at 6:00, so **17)** _____
(I / leave) the office at about 4:45 to go there.

B: So, it seems I'm free this afternoon.

A: No, not exactly. **18)** _____ (you / practice) your speech after I type it. Also,
19) _____ (a computer technician / come) to help you with your computer.
At about 4:00, **20)** _____ (you / go) to a reception for the mayor.
21) _____ (a driver / pick) you up at 3:45.

B: How long is the reception?

A: According to the program, **22)** _____ (it / not / end) until 6:00, so
23) _____ (the driver / come back) for you at 6:05.

B: What time **24)** _____ (my wife / get) here for the dinner?

A: At 6:45. **25)** _____ (she / bring) a clean shirt and tie. Any more questions?

B: No, but thanks for all the arrangements.

Use the words in the boxes to complete the sentences. Use (I'm) going to (do) or (I was) going to (do).

he / have	he / visit	~~I / call~~	~~I / get~~
it / not / be	you / help	you / stay	

1. I've decided to move to a new house.
   I'm going to get _____ a house with a yard.

2. Jason is mad at me for not calling him last night.
   I was going to call _____ him, but it was late, so I decided not to.

3. I think you will enjoy your trip to Hawaii.
   Where _____ ?

4. I miss my brother a lot.
   _____ me this weekend, but there were no flights.

5. Jason drives too fast and doesn't pay attention.
   _____ an accident.

6. Did you move all this furniture alone?
   Yes, _____ me last night, but I guess you forgot.

7. Amy is marrying a man who is much older than she is and who comes from another country.
   I'm worried that _____ an easy marriage.

I / not / quit	I / sell	they / go	they / take	we / eat	we / fix

8. I have changed my mind about my job.
   I'm happy there, so _____ .

9. My parents aren't going to visit me this month.
   _____ to Mexico instead.

10. The sinks in the kitchen and bathroom don't work.
    When _____ them?

11. I feel sorry for my aunt and uncle.
    _____ a trip, but my uncle got sick.

12. I've had this car for 10 years.
    _____ it, but I decided to keep it.

13. I'm getting hungry.
    What time _____ dinner?

Complete the dialogs with words from the boxes. Use *will*, *won't*, or *shall*.
Add necessary words.

ask	be	~~come~~	disturb	get	~~know~~	~~turn~~

1. *A:* Is Sam here yet?

   B: No, but ___he'll___ probably ___come___ soon.

2. *A:* ___Shall I turn___ the air conditioning on?

   B: No, that's all right. I'm comfortable.

3. *A:* When are we leaving on vacation?

   B: Next Monday or Tuesday. ___I won't know___ until I talk to my boss.

4. *A:* Do you know what's wrong with the car?

   B: No, but _____ Tim. He knows everything about cars.

5. *A:* I don't want anyone to come in this room while I'm studying.

   B: Don't worry. I promise no one _____ you.

6. *A:* This book isn't very interesting.

   B: _____ you a different one when I go to the library?

7. *A:* Do you think _____ warm this afternoon?

   B: Yes, I'm sure it will. You won't need a jacket.

call	cost	do	have	need	rain

8. *A:* I don't think we should paint the house ourselves.

   B: Well, how much _____ to have someone paint it?

9. *A:* _____ me a favor?

   B: I'll try. What do you need?

10. *A:* What time _____ me?

    B: After work. Around 6:00, I guess. Will you have your cell phone with you?

11. *A:* Should we buy one chicken or two?

    B: I think _____ two. There will be six of us at dinner.

12. *A:* I'm really hungry tonight.

    B: I am, too. What _____ for dinner? Fish?

13. *A:* I hope it doesn't rain for our picnic tomorrow.

    B: Don't worry. I'm sure _____ . The forecast* says it will be dry.

*forecast: *report about the weather for the future*

Complete the sentences. Use the verb in parentheses and *will* or *going to*. Add any necessary words.

1. We __*are going to buy*__ (buy) a new car next September when we return from our trip.

2. *A:* Amy lost her job.

   B: Really? She __*won't have*__ (not / have) any trouble finding another one.

3. *A:* I see there's a For Sale sign in front of your house.

   B: Yes, now that all our children are away at college, my wife and I _____
   _____ (move) to a smaller house.

4. *(on the phone)* Why didn't you let me know* you were in the hospital? I _____
   _____ (come) and see you after work tonight.

5. *A:* Mike called you, but he'll be in a meeting until 4:00 p.m.

   B: I know. We talked just before the meeting. We _____
   (not / get together) until he's finished with it.

6. Sue's picking me up to go shopping soon. We _____ (stop) at the
   drugstore. Do you need anything?

7. *A:* It's Uncle John's birthday next week.

   B: Is it? I _____ (buy) a card to send him.

8. Sam and Sheila just moved into a new house. _____ (have) a party
   to celebrate.

9. I'm sorry I forgot your birthday. I _____ (make) dinner for you
   some time next week to make it up to you.*

10. *A:* We need a new suitcase for our trip.

    B: I know. That's why I _____ (go) to the store this afternoon.

11. Mike and Amy have changed their minds. They _____ (not / get)
    married after all.*

12. *A:* *(in an office)* Jack's been late to work twice this week. _____
    (you / speak) to him about it, please?

    B: All right. _____ (do) it as soon as he comes in.

13. *A:* Have you decided yet? _____ (you / visit) your mom tonight?

    B: No, I called her. She has other plans. _____ (have) dinner with
    my brother and his wife tonight.

14. *A:* These suitcases weigh a lot.

    B: Let me help you. I _____ (carry) one for you.

*let me know: *tell me*   *make it up to somebody: *do something good for someone you have upset*
*after all: *in spite of what was decided before; in the end*

Future

Circle the most appropriate form of the verb.

1. Hurry up! The movie starts in 15 minutes. We get / are getting / (are going to get) there late.

2. My brother is getting tired of his job. He quits / is quitting / is going to quit when he finds a new one.

3. *A:* Shall we invite Sam to the party?
   B: Why? He doesn't come / isn't coming / won't come. He hates parties.

4. *A:* Hurry up! The bus is almost here.
   B: I will come / come / 'm coming.

5. *A:* The electric bill is due tomorrow.
   B: It is? I am paying / am going to pay / will pay it tonight, then.

6. I'd like to go hiking, but I think it rains / is raining / is going to rain this afternoon.

7. Ana needs to be more careful when she cooks. She burns / is burning / is going to burn herself if she isn't more careful.

8. I am not going to Los Angeles with my wife this weekend because my soccer team plays / is playing / is going to play in a tournament on Saturday morning.

9. We can't use the washer today, but the repairman comes / is coming / is going to come to fix it at 9:00 tomorrow morning.

10. *A:* Should we ask Mike if this movie is good?
    B: No, he doesn't go to movies. He doesn't have / won't have / isn't going to have any idea if we ask him.

11. We left the house late, and there's lots of traffic. I'm afraid we arrive / are arriving / are going to arrive at the doctor's late.

12. *A:* Have you told anyone that I lost my job?
    B: No. Don't worry. I don't tell / am not telling / won't tell anyone.

13. *A:* Your birthday will be / is going to be / is next week. What do you want to do?
    B: Some other friends have already asked me out. They will take / are taking / take me to dinner and a play. Perhaps we can do something together another night if you're free.

14. *A:* Should we open the window for some air?
    B: That isn't making / won't make / doesn't make any difference. It's hot outside, too.

15. Bob and I started taking a cooking class last month. We learn / are learning / are going to learn how to make Chinese food.

16. *A:* *(on the phone)* What did Josh say about going to the mountains next weekend?
    B: Sorry, I completely forgot to ask him. Wait just a second and I will ask / ask / am going to ask him right now.

Will be doing and will have done

Read about Debbie's morning. Then, on the next page, write sentences using *will be doing* and *will have done* with the words in parentheses and other necessary words.

7:30 a.m.–8:00 a.m.

8:00 a.m.–8:15 a.m.

8:15 a.m.–8:45 a.m.

9:00 a.m.–10:00 a.m.

10:00 a.m.–11:00 a.m.

11:00 a.m.–11:30 a.m.

Debbie's routine* doesn't change much from day to day. Debbie and her husband, Greg, get up at 7:00 a.m. and take showers. At 7:30, Debbie gives their baby a bath while Greg makes breakfast. Greg and Debbie eat together at 8:00 before he leaves for work at 8:15. After he leaves, Debbie feeds the baby, and that takes about a half hour. Then she does the breakfast dishes while her baby plays. At 9:00, while the baby is taking a nap,* Debbie does housework. At 10:00, she takes the baby for a walk until 11:00. Debbie watches a TV program from 11:00 to 11:30 while the baby plays on the floor. Then she cooks lunch. She and the baby have lunch from 12:00 to 12:30.

EXERCISE CONTINUES ▶▶

*routine: *usual way of doing things*   *take a nap: *to sleep for a short time, usually during the day*

1. At 7:10
   a. (Debbie / take / a shower) _Debbie will be taking a shower._
   b. (she / already / get up) _She will already have gotten up._
   c. (Greg / not / sleep) _Greg won't be sleeping._

2. At 7:45
   a. (Greg / make / breakfast) _____
   b. (Debbie / give / her baby a bath) _____
   c. (they / not / eat / breakfast yet) _____

3. At 8:10
   a. (they / eat / breakfast) _____
   b. (the baby / finish / her bath) _____
   c. (Greg / not / leave / for work yet) _____

4. At 8:30
   a. (Greg / leave / for work) _____
   b. (Debbie / finish / eating breakfast) _____
   c. (Debbie / feed / the baby) _____

5. At 9:15
   a. (the baby / take / a nap) _____
   b. (Debbie / clean / the house) _____
   c. (the baby / have / her breakfast) _____

6. At 10:30
   a. (they / take / a walk together) _____
   b. (the baby / ride / in a stroller) _____
   c. (they / not / get / back home) _____

7. At 11:15
   a. (they / return / from their walk) _____
   b. (Debbie / watch / TV) _____
   c. (the baby / play / on the floor) _____

Complete the sentences. Use a verb from the box in the simple present or in the future with *will*. Some sentences are negative.

~~feel~~	find out	get	go	paint
~~promise~~	~~rain~~	reach	save	stop

1. You _will feel_ better when you've had something to eat.

2. My brother will lend my sister the money she needs if she _promises_ to pay him back in a month.

3. If there are no clouds in the sky tonight, it probably _won't rain_ tomorrow morning.

4. Can I stay at your place until the rain _____ ?

5. Could you please get me some envelopes when you _____ to the store?

6. Mark will tell us the results of his lab tests* as soon as he _____ about them.

7. I won't buy new clothes if I _____ the job I applied for.

8. *(on an airplane)* Please stay in your seats until the plane _____ the terminal.

9. Max is going to build a fence around the yard when he _____ enough money.

10. They _____ the outside of the house until the weather is drier.

apologize	apply	bother	call	decide
grow up	happen	hurry	move	regret

11. Will your sister buy a house when she _____ to Seattle?

12. Let me know* as soon as you _____ which movie you're going to.

13. I don't think you _____ it if you buy that book. It's wonderful.

14. If you _____ , you might make mistakes. Work slowly.

15. If I _____ for this job, do you think I'll get it?

16. Sue is angry. She won't talk to her brother until he _____ .

17. Your life will be easier when your children _____ .

18. Press the red button. If nothing _____ , try the green one.

19. That bee _____ you if you don't move.

20. Kim _____ me when she has finished the report.

*lab tests: *medical tests or analyses (of blood, etc.)*   *let me know: *tell me*

Future

Read the paragraph.

The weather will probably be nice this week. That's good because I am going to paint the outside of my house. A friend is going to help me, and we'll probably need three or four days to finish. My friend is flying here from Miami, and he arrives tomorrow. I'm picking him up at the airport at 10:30 in the morning. Then we're going to decide on the colors and buy the paint. I don't think it will rain. If it rains, I will just show my friend around* Atlanta. We'll have a real vacation instead of a working vacation!

Write a similar paragraph about your plans for the coming week (or another week in the future). Use appropriate verb forms to express the future. Use these questions as a guide:

1. What are you going to do next week?
2. How do you think the weather will be?
3. Will the weather affect your plans? If so, how?
4. Is anyone visiting you next week?
5. What are you going to do (together)?

*show (someone) around (somewhere): *to show someone the sights and attractions of a place*

Can, could, and (be) able to

Complete the sentences with *can* or *could*, if possible. Otherwise, use *be able to*.

1. When I was little, I __could__ ice-skate, but I __could__ not swim well.

2. I __can__ understand Chinese, but I have never __been able to__ speak it.

3. Mike might _____ come for dinner if he doesn't work late tonight.

4. We wanted to see that new Iranian movie last Thursday, but we _____ not see it. I hope we will _____ see it next week.

5. I was sitting in the back, so I _____ not hear the professor very well. After I moved to the front, I _____ understand every word.

6. I didn't use to _____ dance very well, but I _____ do several different dances now.

7. I speak French pretty well, but I'd like to _____ speak Italian, too.

8. I had forgotten my passport, so I _____ not cross the border.

9. I remember meeting that woman somewhere, but I _____ not remember her name. _____ you remember it?

10. Sally didn't do very well on the test, but she _____ pass it.

11. We used to _____ talk to the boss any time we needed to, but we _____ never talk to him now.

12. We realized that our classmate was having trouble with this grammar, and we _____ help him by explaining it with more examples.

13. It was hard to sleep. We _____ not see any airplanes from our hotel, but we _____ hear them all night.

14. Two people were badly burned in the fire, but the police _____ get them to the hospital very quickly.

15. Amy is a good cook, but she has never _____ make an apple pie.

Complete the sentences with *could(n't)* or *could(n't) have* and a verb from the box.

| ask | ~~be~~ | break down | get | have | take | want | ~~work~~ |

1. I suppose I <u>*could work*</u> a little harder. Then my boss would like me better.

2. Everything about the film was wonderful. It <u>*couldn't have been*</u> better.

3. *A:* I don't want fish for dinner again.
   B: Well, we _____ chicken instead.

4. Why didn't you tell us you needed a ride? We _____ you with us. We had lots of room in the car.

5. *A:* Why is the baby crying?
   B: I don't know. She _____ to be picked up and held.

6. We enjoyed our vacation a lot. We _____ for a nicer hotel.

7. I _____ Samia that book for her birthday. The bookstore had no copies.

8. Don't drive my car too fast. It's old and _____ at any moment.

| apply | be | call | eat | go | lose | put | understand |

9. I understand you had to work late, but I waited an hour for you. You _____ me to let me know.*

10. *A:* Sam got the job that was advertised in the paper.
    B: I know. I _____ for it, too, but I didn't feel qualified.

11. Don't complain about the heat. It _____ hotter.

12. I didn't hear about the meeting until the last minute. I _____ anyway. I was training a new employee.

13. No one was hurt in the accident. We were very lucky. All of us _____ our lives.

14. No one _____ why Stan started crying. It was a mystery to all of us.

15. I was so hungry that I _____ the whole pot of soup by myself.

16. Let's buy this rug. We _____ it in the bedroom.

*let me know: *tell me*

Can, could, and (be) able to; Could (do) and could have (done)

Circle the correct form of the verb.

1. When I finished shopping, I could find / (was able to find) / could have found my car in the parking lot, but I can't find / (couldn't find) / couldn't have found my keys.

2. My sister was able to buy / could buy / could have bought an American car, but she bought a Japanese car instead.

3. Lucia can't speak / couldn't speak / couldn't have spoken English very well last year, but she can have / could have / could have had long conversations in English now.

4. The chef and the waiter were arguing loudly in the restaurant. I can hear / could hear / could have heard everything they said to each other. It was embarrassing.

5. We could stay / were able to stay / could have stayed at the party a lot longer, but my wife and I were both tired, so we went home at 9:30.

6. Jason isn't at work today. It can mean / could mean / could have meant that he's sick again.

7. Please give the tickets back to me if you can't use / couldn't use / didn't manage to use them tomorrow. I'll give them to someone else.

8. Amy can't find / couldn't find / hasn't been able to find an apartment since she moved here.

9. Can you find / Were you able to find / Could you find the person you were looking for?

10. Can you do / Could you have done / Were you able to do me a favor later when you're free?

11. I could get / was able to get / could have gotten an appointment with the dentist today when I explained how bad my toothache was.

12. Lisa could borrow / was able to borrow / could have borrowed my book, but she didn't want to.

13. My boss spoke so fast on the phone that I can't understand / couldn't understand / couldn't have understood what he wanted.

14. Tim didn't want to go to the movies with us last night, but I might be able to / was finally able to / could finally persuade him to go.

15. I can go with you, but I couldn't / won't be able to / haven't been able to drive.

16. Tim runs fast, but he couldn't / hasn't been able to / may not be able to win many races so far.

17. Could you / Have you been able to / Can you drive when you were 16?

18. Marianne was very upset, but no one could understand / could have understood / is able to understand what was bothering her.

Must (You must be tired, etc.)

Read the situation. Use the words in parentheses to write a second sentence with **must** or **must not** in an appropriate tense.

1. Paul hasn't played tennis for ages. (have / trouble)
   He _must be having trouble_ with his back.

2. Jerry knows everything about the stars and planets. (study / astronomy)
   He went to college. He _must have studied astronomy_ there.

3. Your boss and his wife never mention anything about children. (have / children)
   They _must not have children_ .

4. The Carvers' car is never outside their house on Sunday mornings. (go / to church)
   They _____ or out to breakfast then.

5. Jack and Alice always invite me to dinner on Sundays when they're in town. I haven't heard from them this week. (be / here)
   They _____ .

6. Sam has taken the bus to work every day this week. (run / well these days)
   His car _____ .

7. Sheila was married when I met her, but she tells people she's single now. (get / divorced)
   She _____ .

8. Joe is usually so happy, but he's been sad lately. (bother / him)
   Something _____ .

9. They gave everyone at work new dictionaries last Friday, but Paul still doesn't have one. (be / at work last Friday)
   Paul _____ .

10. On his way home, Al turned left instead of right on his street. (think / about something else)
    He _____ .

11. I told you all about the plans for our trip to Italy yesterday. Now you're saying it's the first time you've heard them!? (listen / to me / last night)
    You _____ .

12. I don't recognize anything on either side of the road. (be / the right street)
    This _____ .

13. I said "Tuesday," not "Thursday." (hear / me / correctly)
    You _____ .

14. Sarah isn't paying attention to the teacher. (think / about her date tonight)
    She _____ .

EXERCISE 37

Modals

Can, could, (be) able to, must

UNITS
25–27

Complete the sentences. Use can, could, must or (be) able to + the verb in parentheses.

1. Why didn't you call me? I was free. I __could have taken care of__ (take care of) your children last night.

2. Ask David for money? You __must be joking__ (joke). He never has enough for himself.

3. Why don't you ask your brother for money? He should _____ (lend) you a few hundred dollars.

4. You have chest pains? I'll take you to the emergency room. It _____ (be) something serious.

5. A: I didn't buy that CD last night because I didn't have enough money.
   B: Why didn't you say so? I _____ (lend) you some money.

6. I saw Jeremy driving a shiny new car, but I know he isn't working. He _____ _____ (borrow) the car from someone.

7. A: I asked Sue about her sick father, and she gave a very strange answer.
   B: Maybe there was a good reason for that. She _____ (be) very worried about him, or maybe she was exhausted from taking care of him.

8. Kim divorced her husband and married her brother-in-law?!* You _____ (not / be) serious. Did that really happen?

9. My watch is broken. Would your cousin _____ (fix) it, or does he just work on clocks?

10. I'm so tired that I think I _____ (fall asleep) on the floor.

11. Someone _____ (pick up) my keys by mistake. They were on this table five minutes ago.

12. A: Has Jerry called you back?
    B: Not yet, but I left him three messages yesterday. He _____ (not / check) his messages yesterday, or he would have called back this morning.

13. The Adams's phone bill _____ (be) very high. All their children have cell phones.

14. We're sorry that we won't _____ (attend) your wedding. We'll be out of town that weekend.

15. A: I think Sandra copied from me during the test.
    B: She got a much higher score than you did. She _____ (not / copy) from you.

16. Mr. James says he fought in World War II, but that _____ (not / be) true. He wasn't born until 1940.

40

*brother-in-law: *a husband or wife's brother or a sister's husband*

**Answer each question with two suggestions. Use the words in parentheses + *might*
and *may*. Use *might* in the first sentence and *may* in the second sentence.**

1. *A:* Why is Sam looking at the floor?

   B: 1. (look / for his contact lens) He *might be looking for his contact lens* .

        2. (drop / his contact lens) He *may have dropped his contact lens* .

2. *A:* I can't find my notebook. Have you seen it?

   B: 1. (be / on the bookshelf) It *might be on the bookshelf* .

        2. (forget / it at school) You _____ .

3. *A:* Why does Sarah look so sad today?

   B: 1. (miss / her boyfriend) She _____ .

        2. (have / an argument with her father) _____

        _____ .

4. *A:* Why is Reggie eating so little tonight?

   B: 1. (be / worried about something) He _____ .

        2. (eat / a lot for lunch) _____ .

5. *A:* Isn't Rose coming to the party? She's usually so punctual,* but she's not here yet.

   B: 1. (do / something else tonight) She _____ .

        2. (forget / about the party) _____ .

6. *A:* Why is Bob taking the bus to work these days?

   B: 1. (be / at the mechanic's) His car _____ .

        2. (sell / his car) He _____ .

7. *A:* I wonder how Angela's accident happened.

   B: 1. (not / see / the other car) She _____ .

        2. (not / concentrate / on her driving) _____

        _____ .

8. *A:* I wonder why my grandparents aren't at home.

   B: 1. (go / shopping / for food) _____ .

        2. (be / at the doctor's) _____ .

*punctual: *not late*

May and might

Complete the sentences. Use an appropriate verb in the right form.

1. I thought Carol was joking when she said she was sick yesterday, but she isn't in class today. If she's not in class, she might _be sitting_ in the waiting room at the doctor's right now. I didn't take her seriously, but she may actually _have been_ sick yesterday. She may not _have been joking_ when she said she was sick.

2. If you're waiting for your son to call you, you shouldn't leave your phone turned off. He might _____ you right now, and there's no way you could know.

3. I'm glad we've finished the shopping, but it's too late to start cooking dinner at home now. We might as well _____ at a restaurant.

4. Tom doesn't usually forget things, but he's been very busy at work recently. He may not _____ to call his grandparents last night.

5. Sheila never comes this late to a party, but she often babysits on weekends. She might _____ tonight.

6. It's strange that the Smiths sold their car, because they used to use it a lot. They may not _____ to get along without it.

7. A: Where's Dan?
   B: I don't know. He was talking about working in the yard. He may _____ the grass in the backyard.

8. A: It costs a lot to rent a house in this city.
   B: Yes, it does. If you can afford to, you may as well _____ a house.

9. A: Didn't Sally say she was going to wait for us here?
   B: I don't remember. She might _____ for us at the restaurant. Let's go there.

10. Watch out. It's icy outside. You might _____ on the ice and hurt yourself.

11. You might _____ wear your brother's suit to the wedding if you lose a little weight first.

12. A: Have you decided what you're going to do on your day off?
    B: Not yet. We may _____ to the beach, or we may just _____ home.

13. A: Why do you think our teacher got angry with us last night?
    B: Who knows? She may not _____ well.

Answer these questions with your own words in complete sentences.

1. A friend has graduated from college in computer science but hasn't found a job. Suggest what your friend could do to get a job.

    You could go to Canada and try to find a job there. (OR You could go back to school for another degree. OR You and I could start a business together.)

2. Where will you be living 10 years from now? If you are not sure, where might you be living?

3. What might you be doing 10 years from now?

4. What could you do when you were little that you can't do now?

5. Is there a sport or other activity that you tried to learn when you were little but weren't able to learn? What was it? How did you try to learn it? Why weren't you able to learn it?

6. What might happen to the world if we cannot learn to live together peacefully?

7. What may happen if we do not solve the problem of global warming?

8. Could countries like China, Germany, and the United States have developed without harming the environment? Why or why not?

9. Think of someone who's living in another country. What time is it there right now, and what may that person be doing? If you're quite sure, tell what that person must be doing.

10. Imagine that you got together with a group of friends last week. A good friend there refused to speak to you. What may or must have happened to make your friend act that way?

Have to and **must**

Are the underlined parts of the sentences right or wrong? Correct the wrong ones.

1. Sorry I missed class. I <u>have got to work</u> late
   last night.   *had to work*

2. Passengers on an airplane <u>must not leave</u> their
   seats during takeoff and landing.   *RIGHT*

3. You <u>have got to help</u> me. No one else will.   _____

4. The students <u>must not buy</u> new books for the
   course. They can use the ones from last semester. _____

5. My father said I <u>don't have to use</u> his new car
   under any circumstances.*   _____

6. I <u>will have to do</u> my homework over if the
   teacher isn't happy with it.   _____

7. Jim said, "Sorry I can't stay any longer. I'<u>ve got
   to leave</u> the party early to pick someone up at
   the airport."   _____

8. I <u>must not work</u> next Saturday, so I guess I can go
   to the beach with you.   _____

9. Paul <u>has had to go</u> to Tokyo on business twice
   already this year.   _____

10. People <u>must not take</u> the hostess* a present when
    they are invited to dinner in the U.S., but it's
    considered polite.   _____

11. <u>Did I have to work</u> on the weekend if I can't
    finish this today?   _____

12. Applications <u>must be</u> received by the end of
    this month.   _____

13. <u>Had Cal and Lena to move</u>, or did they want to? _____

14. You <u>must try</u> to drive more carefully. The
    accident was your fault.   _____

15. We <u>might have to get up</u> early if Ted asks us to
    take him to the airport tomorrow morning.   _____

16. Ben <u>must take</u> his wife to the hospital in the
    middle of the night last week.   _____

*not under any circumstances: *in no case; never*   *hostess: *woman who receives others as guests in her home*

Complete the sentences with *should* (*have*) + the verb in parentheses in the correct form.

1. If you're unhappy with your present job, I think you __*should look*__ (look) for another one tomorrow.

2. Aren't you cold in just a shirt? You __*should be wearing*__ (wear) a sweater in weather like this.

3. Jerry spoke angrily to his boss and lost his job. Jerry __*shouldn't have lost*__ (lose) his temper.*

4. You've known all week that we were driving to the city today. You _____ _____ (buy) gas before.

5. The bad weather will slow us down, but we _____ (get) there before dark.

6. Ted's in the cafeteria drinking coffee again. He _____ (work). He _____ (not / take) a break.

7. Andrew has exams this morning, but I saw him out dancing last night. He _____ (study) for his exams.

8. I am really worried about the children. They _____ (be) here an hour ago.

9. It's a popular movie, but we _____ (not / have) much trouble getting tickets on a Monday afternoon. Let's go.

10. The boss got angry at Ben because he was talking on his cell phone during the meeting. Ben _____ (not / talk) on his cell phone then.

11. This book is overdue.* You _____ (return) it to the library last week.

12. I know you're upset, but don't you think you _____ (think) about it a little more before quitting your job?

13. Your report is due tomorrow, and you're watching TV?! You _____ _____ (not / watch) TV. You _____ (work) on that report.

14. The accident was my fault. I was talking on my cell phone when I _____ _____ (pay) attention to the traffic.

*lose your temper: *not to be able to control your anger*   *overdue: *not returned on time*   45

Subjunctive (**I suggest you do**)

Jerry broke his leg and will be wearing a cast for a while. Read the advice he got from various people. Then write what each person suggested or recommended he do.

His teacher: "Do your homework if you feel well enough."

His father: "We need to make you comfortable at home."

The nurse: "It's important for you not to try to walk without crutches."

His mother: "You have to drink a lot of milk to make your bones strong."

His friend from school: "Why don't you call me every day to get the homework?"

His brother: "You should be given aspirin if your leg hurts a lot."

The doctor: "You absolutely must not walk on your leg for three days."

His sister: "You needed to stay in the hospital longer."

crutches   cast

1. His teacher suggested that he ___*do his homework*___ if he feels well enough.

2. His father said it was necessary that Jerry ___*be made comfortable at home*___ .

3. The nurse said it was important that he not _____ .

4. His mother said it was essential _____ .

5. His friend proposed that Jerry _____ .

6. His brother recommended Jerry _____ if his leg hurts a lot.

7. The doctor said it was imperative _____ .

8. His sister thought it was necessary _____ .

Should; Had better; It's time . . .

A. Put in _had better_ where appropriate. If _had better_ is not appropriate, use _should_.

1. You _had better_ be careful. That ladder you are on might fall.

2. Sandra and Ted often leave their door unlocked. They _should_ be more careful.

3. The children _____ be in bed when we get home, or they'll be sorry.

4. Most American parents think children _____ have a regular bedtime, especially on school nights.

5. We _____ invite George to the party, or his feelings will be hurt.

6. We _____ get to the box office early, or we won't get tickets to the play.

7. I don't think anyone under the age of 18 _____ drive.

8. Don't you think people _____ use their cars less to reduce pollution?

9. Parents whose teenagers are allowed to have parties at home _____ always supervise the parties.

10. They might have closed the mountain road because of the snow. We _____ call the police before we leave to make sure the road is open.

B. Rewrite the sentences. Use _It's time_.

1. Amy has had a cold for weeks. I think she should see a doctor very soon.
   It's time Amy saw a _____ doctor.

2. Our TV is 15 years old. We should buy a new one.
   It's time we _____ a new TV.

3. We really need to do something about homeless people in this country.
   _____ about homeless people in this country.

4. It's getting late. Let's go home.
   _____ home.

5. You're an adult now. You should be more responsible.
   _____ responsible.

6. It's almost 7:30. We should have had dinner before now.
   _____ dinner.

Read the situation. Then complete the sentences with *will* (*won't*) or *would* (*wouldn't*) and the words in parentheses.

1. Jeremy is looking forward to getting a new bicycle when he gets paid next week. His old one breaks down a lot, and he depends on a bike to get to work. Of course, his dream is to have a car, but he can't afford one. Riding his bike in traffic scares him, however.

   a. (get a new bike) *Jeremy will get a new bike soon* _____ .

   b. (love to have a car) *He would love to have a car* _____ .

   c. (make his life easier) The new bike _____ .

   d. (be safer) His trip to work _____ in a car.

   e. (not / buy a new car) He probably _____ any time soon.

2. The Jones family is pretty big. Mr. and Mrs. Jones have three children of their own, and they have adopted* two others. The Joneses are sorry they don't have even more children. The children's education is important, so the parents are saving money to send all of them to college.

   a. (all have a chance) The Jones children _____ to go to college.

   b. (be happy) The Joneses don't have six or seven children, but they _____ _____ with that many.

   c. (not / be happy) The Joneses _____ with just one or two children.

   d. (probably get good jobs) The children _____ after college.

3. Mrs. Gupta has worked since she got married. She has three young children and feels guilty* that she's not a mother who stays home. But the family needs the money because her husband doesn't earn a lot.

   a. (not / feel guilty) Maybe Mrs. Gupta should stay home. Then she _____ _____ .

   b. (not / quit) She probably _____ her job.

   c. (not / continue working) Her husband might find a better job. Then she probably _____ .

   d. (go to work) I suppose she _____ tomorrow as usual.

   e. (be a solution) Her sister might move to Chicago to help with the children. That _____ to Mrs. Gupta's problem.

*adopt: *to accept someone else's child into a family through a legal process*   *guilty: *unhappy because of doing something you think is wrong*

Modals

Complete the conversation using the words in parentheses. Use the appropriate tense. Add other necessary words.

Carol is talking to her friend Sally, who has caught a bad cold.

Carol: Did your doctor tell you to stay home from work?

Sally: No, but she 1) *recommended I rest* (recommend / I / rest) a lot.
She said 2) *I should try* (I / should / try) to sleep 10 hours a day.

Carol: Did she write you a prescription?

Sally: No, 3) _____ (I / not / have to / take) any medicine. It will just take time and rest for my cold to get better.

Carol: How will you manage to rest when you work all day?

Sally: The doctor 4) _____ (suggest / I / relax) at my desk during lunch. And she 5) _____ (recommend / I / take) a nap* at home after work.

Carol: 6) _____ (can / I / do) anything to help you?

Sally: 7) _____ (that / would / be) wonderful!
8) _____ (could / you / come over) and watch my kids for an hour after work for two or three days?
9) _____ (my husband / have to / work) until 7:00 most nights, so he can't help.

Carol: 10) _____ (I / would / be) glad to help.
11) _____ (should / I / come) at about 5:30?

Sally: Perfect. 12) _____ (I / had better / call) their piano teacher to say they'll miss their lesson, or he'll be worried about them.

Carol: 13) _____ (could / I / take) the kids to their lesson for you?

Sally: No, that's all right. It's 14) _____ (time / they / spend) a little more time on their schoolwork anyway. They really 15) _____ (should / put) more effort into their math and reading.

Carol: Is there anything else that you need?

Sally: No, thanks.

*take a nap: to sleep for a short time, usually during the day

Complete the sentences about yourself and others.

1. There are times when a person shouldn't _tell the truth_ _____ .
    There are times when a person shouldn't _ask too many questions_ _____ .
    There are times when a person shouldn't _____ .

2. In my opinion, parents should always _____ .

3. I have one regret. I shouldn't have _____ .

4. When driving a car, people ought _____ .

5. We had better _____ , or global
    warming will get worse.

6. There are two things I would never ask another person:
    a. Would _____ ?
    b. Could you _____ ?

7. I have never had to _____
    _____ .

8. When a friend complains too much about her husband, I usually say to her: "It's time you
    _____ ."

9. When I have a problem, my family usually insists _____
    _____ .

10. A friend of mine suggested that I _____ .

11. To make a better world, it's important that we all _____
    _____ .

12. It's time that the people in my country _____
    _____ .

13. Once I told a friend that he'd/she'd better _____
    _____ .

14. When I was little, my father would always _____
    _____ .

15. In a disaster like a flood or a tsunami, people mustn't _____
    _____ .

If I do . . . and If I did . . .

Read the paragraph about a bad boss. Complete the *if*-sentences using the information in the paragraph.

Frank is not a very popular boss because he doesn't respect his workers. He is not honest, so we don't trust him. He isn't efficient because he's so disorganized. He never knows where things are, so he has to ask his secretary. Most people don't work hard because he gives raises to people he likes, not to people who work hard. He doesn't answer questions clearly, so we never really understand him. He tells different stories to different people, so we never know what is going on. He has a lot of meetings that last past working hours, so we can't go home on time. Sometimes the meetings last two hours, so we all get home late for dinner. We get confused because he changes his mind all the time. We are all afraid because no one feels secure about their job. Frank is a terrible boss, so we are all going to look for other jobs.

1. Frank would be a more popular boss _if he respected his workers_ .

2. If Frank were honest, _we would trust him_ .

3. If he weren't so disorganized, _____ .

4. He wouldn't have to ask his secretary if _____ .

5. If he gave raises fairly, _____ .

6. We would understand him _____ .

7. We would know what was going on if _____ .

8. If he didn't have a lot of late meetings, _____ .

9. We wouldn't be late for dinner if _____ .

10. If he didn't change his mind all the time, _____ .

11. We wouldn't be afraid _____ .

12. We wouldn't all look for other jobs if _____ .

If I knew . . . , I wish I knew . . .

Use the words in parentheses to write what each person wishes for now. Put the verb in the correct form. Some sentences are negative.

1. (have / a broken leg)

   Kerry wishes _she didn't have a broken leg_ .

2. (be / married)

   Sylvia _wishes she was/were married_ .

3. (work / in an office)

   Mike wishes _____ .

4. (rain / outside / right now)

   I wish it _____ .

5. (can / afford / a new car)

   Kevin and Sue _____ .

EXERCISE CONTINUES ▶▶

6. (live / near the ocean)
Brandon _____ .

7. (own / a car)
Alfred _____ .

8. (have / only one cat)
Mary Jo _____ .

9. (have to / get up / so early)
Julio and Marta _____ .

10. (be / so expensive)
A lot of people wish gas _____ .

If and *Wish*

If I had known . . . , I wish I had known . . .

Read A's questions. Then complete B's answer with a statement using *if*.

1. *A:* Why didn't Frank go to Hawaii? Didn't he have enough money?
   B: No. *If he'd had enough money, he would have gone to Hawaii.*

2. *A:* Why didn't Joe's family eat his soup? Was there too much salt in it?
   B: Yes. *If there hadn't been too much salt in it, Joe's family would have eaten it.*

3. *A:* Why didn't the tourists go swimming yesterday? Was it a stormy day?
   B: Yes. _____
   _____

4. *A:* Why didn't Regina hear the teacher's announcement? Wasn't she in class?
   B: No. _____
   _____

5. *A:* Why didn't Sid eat breakfast? Did he get up late?
   B: Yes. _____
   _____

6. *A:* Why didn't the Smiths receive the package yesterday? Weren't they at home?
   B: No. _____
   _____

7. *A:* Why didn't Jessica buy her groceries yesterday? Was she on her bike?
   B: Yes. _____
   _____

8. *A:* Why didn't Bob look up the new word? Wasn't he able to find his dictionary?
   B: No. _____
   _____

9. *A:* Why didn't you call me on my birthday? Did you forget?
   B: Yes. _____
   _____

10. *A:* Why didn't you and Cal go to Joe's party last week? Didn't you know about it?
    B: No. _____
    _____

If I knew . . . , I wish I knew . . . ; If I had known . . . ; I wish I had known . . .

Write sentences with *wish* + the words in parentheses. Some sentences are about the present, and some are about the past. Some sentences are negative.

1. I'm very hungry.
   (skip* breakfast this morning) *I wish I hadn't skipped breakfast this morning* .
   (have something to eat now) *I wish I had something to eat now* .

2. Maria is angry at me.
   (not / be angry at me) I wish she _____ .
   (tell other people her secret) I wish I _____ .

3. We didn't accept the Lees' dinner invitation.
   (accept it) I wish we _____ .
   (eat dinner there now) _____ .

4. What you said hurt my feelings.
   (say it) I wish you _____ .
   (be so sensitive all the time) I wish I _____ .

5. I didn't know you were in the hospital last week.
   (tell me) I wish someone _____ .
   (not / live so far away) I wish you _____ .

6. I can't go away for a vacation this year.
   (spend so much money on my car) _____ .
   (can afford to spend time in the mountains) _____ .

7. It's raining now.
   (be nicer today) I wish it _____ .
   (bring my umbrella this morning) _____ .

8. Ted decided to change jobs very quickly.
   (have more time to think about it) He wishes _____ .
   (have to make decisions so quickly all the time) He _____
   _____ .

9. My cousin is getting married in Panama, but I don't have enough money to go.
   (be able to go) _____ .
   (save money this past year) _____ .

---

*skip: *to decide to miss an event or activity*

If and *Wish*

Wish

Are these sentences right or wrong? Correct them where necessary.

1. I wish you a safe trip.   _RIGHT_

2. I wish you have a safe trip.   _I hope you have a safe trip._

3. Get well soon. I wish you wouldn't feel so bad.   _I wish you didn't feel so bad._

4. Todd wishes he studied something else when he was in college.

5. I wish you wouldn't talk to me during the movie. I can't hear what's going on.

6. Kim wishes she would like her job better.

7. Enjoy the party. I wish you have a nice time.

8. I wish you'd take these tickets – they won't be used otherwise.

9. I wish you stopped talking for a few minutes so that I can think.

10. The weather's been wonderful. I wish it continues that way.

11. I wish I don't have to go to work today, but they're waiting for me.

12. I wish my alarm clock wouldn't be so loud. It scares me in the morning.

13. My sister wishes her husband would stop complaining.

14. Our trip was only for a week. I wish we can spend more time in Guatemala, but we had to come home.

15. "Wish me luck on my exam," Tom said to us as he entered the exam room.

16. I made the wrong decision. I wish I thought about it more.

17. I wish there are fewer people in my English class.

18. I was looking forward to the party. I wish it hadn't been canceled.

If and wish

Use your own ideas to complete the sentences about yourself.

1. You probably don't have everything you would like to have or feel exactly the way you'd like to feel. What don't you have? What would you do if you had it?

   If I _had a car_____ , I would _learn to drive_____ .

   If I _wasn't tired_____ , I would _go out tonight_____ .

   If I _____ , I would _____ .

2. Is there enough food and fresh water for everyone in the world? Is there enough peace and good will? What wish can you make for the world?

   I wish there were _____ .

3. Is your family completely satisfied with everything you do, or is there something they might change about you? If yes, say what they wish.

   My family wishes I would _____ .

4. Is there something you can't do that you want to? What is stopping you?

   I could _____ if _____ .

5. Have you done something that you regret because you didn't know something you should have known? Write about it.

   I wouldn't have _____ if I had known _____ .

6. Have you given advice to a friend recently? What did you think that person should do? How would their life be different?

   I said to a friend recently, "You'd _____ if you'd

   _____ ."

7. Did you do something last month that you regret now? If yes, what do you wish now?

   I wish I hadn't _____ last month.

8. Did you do something when you were younger that you regret now? For example, do you have less money now or fewer friends because of what you did?

   I would _____ now if I had _____

   _____ when I was younger.

9. We all have hopes for the future, a desire for things possibly to be different than they are now. What hope do you have for the world?

   I hope that _____ .

10. What happens in our lives sometimes results from something we didn't do. Write about a situation like that in your own life.

    I might have _____ if I had _____ .

Passive

Passive (is done / was done)

Complete the sentences with the words in parentheses. Use passive verbs in the simple present or the simple past.

1. You have to pay extra for the batteries. (they / not / include) *They aren't included* in the price of the flashlight.

2. (Mrs. Chen's dog / kill) _____ in an accident. She is very sad.

3. (elections / hold) How often _____ in the United States?

4. (Mary / fire*) _____ for missing work too often.

5. (flights / sometimes / cancel) _____ when the weather is bad.

6. (I / accuse) _____ of exaggerating, but I only told the truth about the accident.

7. (your sweater / make) Where _____ ? It's very nice.

8. (not / know) It _____ at this time whether the hikers have enough food.

9. (the accident / cause) The police said _____ by a drunk driver.

10. (the first satellite / send) _____ into space by the Americans or the Russians?

11. (The letter *v* / not / pronounce) _____ the same in Spanish and English, so be careful.

12. (baseball games / cancel) How many times last year _____ _____ because of rain?

13. (many houses / damage) _____ by floods every year.

14. (my camera / not / steal) Fortunately, _____ in the robbery.

15. (we / warn) When we left the hotel, _____ to be careful with our wallets and passports.

16. (this thing / use) What _____ for? Is it something for your bike?

17. (you / take) Why _____ to the hospital after the accident?

fire: to tell somebody they don't have a job anymore

Passive (**is done / was done**); Passive (**be done / been done / being done**)

Complete B's answers. Use a passive form of the verb in parentheses.

A

B

1. Were you watching the baseball game at 4:00 p.m. yesterday?

(fix) No, I wasn't able to. My TV _was being_ _fixed_ then.

2. What happened to Pete? He's black and blue* all over.

(injure) I heard he had an accident. He must _____ _____ then.

3. The bills aren't due until next week, right?

(pay) No. They should _____ _____ immediately.

4. Have you cleaned the refrigerator recently?

(clean) No. I don't think it _____ _____ for weeks.

5. Are they going to build the new highway this year?

(build) No. It _____ _____ next year.

6. Did your parents' grandparents come to this country on a plane?

(invent) No, by ship. I don't think the airplane _____ _____ yet.

7. Did the police find any evidence* at the scene of the crime?*

(find) No. But some evidence will probably _____ _____ nearby.

8. Should I take your sweater to the cleaner's?

(wash) Yes, please. I don't think it can _____ _____ in water.

9. Was the boss making a joke or criticizing us?

(criticize) I definitely think we _____ _____ .

10. Did anyone notify the police after the accident last night?

(call) No. The police should _____ _____ immediately, but they weren't.

11. Did anyone deliver a package for me today?

(deliver) I don't know. A package might _____ _____ , but I haven't seen one.

12. Do you use this computer much?

(use) No, I don't think it _____ for several months.

13. Can you give me any advice about teaching?

(need) All I know is that patience and caring _____ _____ .

*black and blue: *with dark marks on your skin caused by being hit or by an accident*   *evidence: *something that provides information about a crime*   *scene of the crime: *the place where a crime happened*

Passive (**is done** / **was done**); Passive (**be done** / **been done** / **being done**)

Read the passage about Tony's job. Then complete the passage using the verbs in parentheses. Sometimes the verb is active, sometimes passive.

My friend Tony has had a lot of problems in his job at a telephone company.
He 1) _was hired_ (hire) two months ago, and everything 2) _started_ (start) out
perfectly. He 3) _____ (work) very hard in the beginning because he wanted
to please his boss. Tony 4) _____ (ask) by his boss to work overtime, and he
5) _____ (agree). He 6) _____ (come) to work early and
7) _____ (leave) late.

However, up until now he 8) _____ (not / pay) for the extra work.
He 9) _____ (complain) to his boss several times, but nothing
10) _____ (do) about the problem so far. Last week, Tony
11) _____ (ask) for a day off, but his request 12) _____
(refuse). Therefore, he 13) _____ (have to / miss) his brother's high
school graduation. His family, especially his brother, 14) _____ (be)
very disappointed.

When they 15) _____ (hire) him, the company 16) _____
(promise) to pay for computer classes, so Tony 17) _____ (take) a class at the
college all semester. However, when Tony 18) _____ (ask to / reimburse*) for
the class, his boss told him that the company was not paying for classes anymore. Tony felt he
19) _____ (treat) unfairly.

It is clear to Tony that he 20) _____ (will / never / promote) in the company.
Promotions 21) _____ (give) only to the boss's favorites. Tony now
22) _____ (want to / quit) his job, but he 23) _____
(not / want to / give) a bad recommendation when he leaves. Also, he knows it will not look
good if he 24) _____ (leave) a job he has had for only a few months. On the
bright side, Tony 25) _____ (contact) by several other companies recently.
They are looking for people with his experience. He 26) _____ (might / offer)
a job by one of those companies any time now. Should he 27) _____ (accept)
an offer or continue in his present job? What do you think?

*reimburse: *to pay back money to somebody*

Passive 3

Are the underlined parts of these sentences right or wrong? Correct the wrong ones.

1. Volunteers <u>don't get paid</u> for the work they do. _RIGHT_

2. I <u>am biting</u> by mosquitoes more than
   most people. _am bitten_ (OR _get bitten_)

3. My father <u>born</u> in the South, but he grew up
   in the North. _____

4. <u>Did we tell</u> what time the meeting will end?
   I don't remember what the boss said. _____

5. Those teenagers are used to <u>treating</u> like
   adults, and they act that way. _____

6. How often <u>are you paying</u> by your company? _____

7. At what age <u>are children taught</u> to dress
   themselves? _____

8. A job <u>has offered</u> to my brother in
   another country. _____

9. Steve's nose <u>got broken</u> in a fight. _____

10. This soup pot is dusty because it <u>doesn't use</u>
    very much anymore. _____

11. I don't like <u>criticizing</u> publicly by the teacher. _____

12. Rodney <u>is known</u> for helping others. _____

13. Sarah doesn't like being told how to raise
    her children, but she appreciates <u>to help</u> by
    her mother. _____

14. Larry is afraid of <u>getting stopped</u> by the police
    because he doesn't have a license. _____

15. Sally <u>has offered</u> a job with better pay, and
    she'll probably accept it. _____

16. Carol loves <u>getting inviting</u> to people's houses,
    but she never invites people back. _____

Passive

It is said that . . . He is said to . . . (be) supposed to . . .

Choose the sentence on the right that most logically follows the sentence on the left.

_d_ 1. What are you doing at home?

_____ 2. You shouldn't take that medicine until lunchtime.

_____ 3. I'd like to see that Brazilian film we read about.

_____ 4. We've had rain for three days in a row.

_____ 5. How could you vote for a candidate* like her?

_____ 6. They're still looking for the lost hiker.

_____ 7. Why don't you make an appointment with Dr. Cummins?

_____ 8. I don't know why they use plutonium* to generate electricity.

_____ 9. Why don't we go to that hotel in the mountains this weekend?

_____ 10. I'm angry with my daughter.

_____ 11. I don't think you should take so many painkillers.*

_____ 12. It seems the accident wasn't too bad.

_____ 13. You'll have to move your car.

a. It's expected to stop soon, though.

b. You're only supposed to take it with food.

c. She is said to have stolen money.

✓ d. You're supposed to be at work.

e. She's supposed to be very good.

f. It's supposed to be very good.

g. She is believed to have food and water, fortunately.

h. There's supposed to be a lot to do there.

i. They're not supposed to be good for your liver.*

j. It's known to remain dangerous for many years.

k. You're not supposed to park here.

l. She was supposed to wash the dishes, but she didn't.

m. No one was reported to have been seriously injured.

*candidate: *a person who tries to be elected for a political or official position*   *plutonium: *a radioactive chemical element*   *painkillers: *pills that reduce pain*   *liver: *a large organ in the body that cleans the blood*

Have/get something done

Complete the conversations. Use the correct form of *have/get something done* with the phrases in box.

change / our telephone number / get	check / the brakes / have
clean / his house / get	clean / my teeth / have
deliver / the prescription* / have	do / her hair / get
fix / your car / get	install / a solar water heater / have
~~remove / a tattoo / have~~	search / her luggage / have
~~shave / his head / get~~	test / my blood / get

1. *A:* Why is Jeremy going to the barber again so soon? He was there last week.

   B: He wants to _get his head shaved_ .

2. *A:* Is your sister's surgery serious?

   B: Not at all. She's _having a tattoo removed_ .

3. *A:* Will that company ever stop calling us? They're beginning to bother me.

   B: I think we should _____ .

4. *A:* Ashley always looks very nice.

   B: Yes, she does. She _____ every week.

5. *A:* Why is Lisa so upset about her trip?

   B: She _____ three times!

6. *A:* Why are you going to the dentist? Do you have a toothache?

   B: No, I am just going to _____ .

7. *A:* I can't go to the drugstore until after work. Can you wait that long for your medicine?

   B: That's all right. I'll _____ by the pharmacy.

8. *A:* Why is Thomas making so many phone calls at work? Who is he calling?

   B: His parents are coming and the house is a mess. He wants to _____ before then. He's calling cleaners.

9. *A:* Why don't you _____ ? It's very noisy.

   B: I don't have enough money this month.

10. *A:* Are you concerned about the environment?

    B: Yes. That's why I'm going to _____ soon.

11. *A:* Where's your car?

    B: At the mechanic's. I'm _____ .

12. *A:* Why do you have to go to the lab so early? It's only 7:00 a.m.

    B: The doctor wants me to _____ before I eat anything.

*prescription: *a doctor's instruction saying a pharmacist is allowed to sell you a specific medication

Complete the sentences in your own words. Use a passive construction where possible.

1. When we are small, parents and teachers seem to run our lives. What were you made to do? What were you told to do – or not to do?

    When I was little, I was _given a lot of responsibilities by my parents_ .

    When I was little, I was _told by my parents to stop crying all the time_ .

    When I was little, I was _____ .

2. People often expect things of us, but we can't always do what they want us to. What was expected of you last year that you couldn't do?

    Last year, I was supposed to _go to my friend's wedding, but I wasn't able to go_ .

    Last year, I was supposed to _____ , but I wasn't able _____ .

3. Sometimes we don't like the things that people do to us, and they may do them over and over. What has been done to you that you didn't like?

    I really dislike being _____ .

4. Sometimes friends do something to us that we don't want them to do. And sometimes we have to tell them again and again not to do it to us. Give an example from your life.

    I have told my friends many times that I don't want to be _____ .

5. We all have opinions about how criminals should be treated – maybe better or maybe worse than they are. What's your opinion about the treatment of criminals?

    In my opinion, criminals should not be _____ .

6. If we have opinions about criminals, we have even more about children and how they should be treated. What should be done? What should never be done to children?

    Children should be _____ but never _____ .

7. We all have favorite things that we like people to do for us. What is one of yours?

    I love being _____ .

8. There are things that we don't like to do, and if we have enough money, we pay someone to do them for us. Give two examples from your life.

    There are some things I never do myself. For example, I have _____

    _____ and I get _____ .

9. It's not unusual to be afraid that something might happen to us in the future or that someone might do something unpleasant to us. Tell something like that about yourself.

    I'm sometimes afraid that I'll get _____ .

10. Most students have an idea of how they learn best and how they want their lives to be. What would make most students that you know happier?

    Most students would be happier if they were _____ .

Reported Speech (**He said that . . .**)

Read what Kevin said to Don on the phone. Then write what Don told Maggie about his conversation with Kevin. Use reported speech.

✓ 1. "I can't go to the baseball game with you this Saturday."
✓ 2. "I'll be out of town."
3. "I have to go to Toronto."
4. "I don't need the book I lent Maggie because I've already read it."
5. "My son is going to paint my house for me."
6. "My family is doing well."
7. "My father was sick, but he's much better now."
8. "I really enjoyed Maggie's cookies."
9. "I'll see you next Saturday."

Kevin   Don

Don   Maggie

1. *Maggie:* Is Kevin going to go out with us?

   Don: No. *He said (that) he couldn't go to the baseball game with us this Saturday* .

2. *Maggie:* Why not?

   Don: *He said (that) he would be out of town* .

3. *Maggie:* On business?

   Don: I'm not sure. He _____ .

4. *Maggie:* Does Kevin want his book back?

   Don: No. _____ the book because

   _____ .

5. *Maggie:* Does he need any help painting his house?

   Don: No. _____

6. *Maggie:* How's his family?

   Don: _____

7. *Maggie:* Did he say anything about his father?

   Don: Yes. _____ , but

   _____ .

8. *Maggie:* Did he eat the cookies I made for him?

   Don: Yes. _____ .

9. *Maggie:* When will we see him?

   Don: _____ .

Read the sentences in direct speech. Then use them to complete the sentences with reported speech.

Don't forget to call me.   Please wait until he's free.   I like your accent.

Take it easy and relax.   I've been too busy.

You don't have to bring a present.   Charlie has just bought a house.   You'll have to help out more at home.

Please don't tell anyone what I said.   You look just like your grandfather.

1. Jason needs a friend's address urgently, so he asked _me not to forget to call him_ .

2. My grandmother once said _(that) I looked/look just like my grandfather_ .

3. I told the woman from Namibia _____ .

4. Brian was so nervous about meeting the new boss. I told _____ .

5. Jane and her husband wanted advice on buying a house. I told _____ .

6. The doctor was with a patient when I called. The nurse asked _____ .

7. When my mother got sick, my father said _____ .

8. Nicholas apologized for not getting in touch. He said _____ .

9. Sally is afraid of her boss. After she told me about her problems at work, she asked _____ .

10. When she called to invite me to last week's party, Emily said _____ .

Reported Speech

Read the paragraph in which a man tells about his conversation with his sister-in-law.*
Then change the reported speech to direct speech. Use the words in parentheses and any
other necessary words. Be sure to use quotation marks.

My sister-in-law Mona called to complain about her husband, who is my brother. She
said my brother was spending too much time at work. Then she told me he wasn't very
responsible about money. She said he often spent money on himself instead of on her and
the children. She asked me not to tell my brother about our conversation. I told her not to
worry, that I wouldn't say anything to him. I advised her to speak to him honestly but not
to get angry while they were discussing these matters. I said her anger would make him
less likely* to talk openly. She said she would try to follow my advice.

1. (spend / work)

   Mona said, *"Your brother is spending too much time at work."*

2. (responsible / money)

   She said, "He _____

3. (money / himself / me and the children)

   She said, _____

4. (not / conversation)

   She said, "Please _____

5. (worry) (say anything to him)

   I said, _____

6. (honestly) (angry / matters)

   I said, _____ , but _____

   _____

7. (anger / talk openly)

   I said, _____

8. (try / advice)

   She said, _____

---

*sister-in-law: *a brother's wife or a husband or wife's sister* *likely: *probable*

UNITS
45–46

Look at what each person did. Read what each one says. Report what each person said, and then what each person really did.

1. Yesterday morning

1. Martin: "I get up at six every morning."
   Martin said *he got up at six every morning,*
   but he *didn't get up at six yesterday* .

2. Lunchtime yesterday

2. Jason: "I haven't eaten anything all day."
   At dinner last night, Jason said *he hadn't eaten*
   anything all day , but *he ate* something at
   lunchtime yesterday.

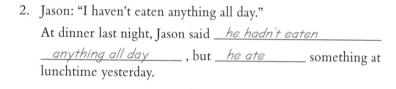

3. Last week

3. Sally: "I always cut my hair myself."
   Sally said _____ , but
   _____ it herself last week.

4. Breakfast this morning

4. Reggie: "I always eat a very small breakfast."
   Reggie said _____ ,
   _____ a lot this morning.

5. Last Thursday morning

5. Jane: "I'm taking the bus to work Thursday morning."
   Jane said _____ ,
   _____ car to work that morning.

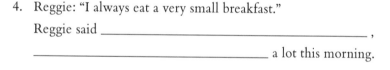

6. Last week

6. Jerry: "I don't know how to play a musical instrument."
   Jerry told me _____ ,
   _____ the guitar last week.

Follow-up: Think of a recent short conversation you've had or one that you overheard. In a paragraph, use reported speech to write what was said. Write on a separate piece of paper.

Questions 1

Complete the conversations by writing B's questions.

	A	**B**

1. You'll never guess who visited my company today.

    I give up. Who _visited your company today_ ?

2. We invited a lot of people to our anniversary party.

    Really? How many _people did you invite_ ?

3. I haven't used my new computer yet.

    But you need it. Why _haven't you used it_ ?

4. More people than we expected came to our party last weekend.

    What a surprise. How many _____ _____ ?

5. They've had their house a long time.

    About how long _____ _____ ?

6. I missed the bus again this morning.

    Too bad. Why _____ ?

7. This road was built a long time ago.

    Exactly when _____ _____ ?

8. I'm looking for a birthday present.

    What kind of _____ _____ ?

9. Someone forgot their notebook.

    Who _____ _____ ?

10. Zoe isn't going to take her test.

    Why _____ _____ ?

11. Jack bought another new car.

    What kind of _____ _____ ?

12. Helen didn't say hello to me this morning.

    That's strange. Why _____ _____ ?

13. Marge earns a lot more money than her husband.

    How much _____ _____ ?

14. Roger won't return my phone calls.

    Why _____ _____ ?

Questions and Auxiliary Verbs

Questions 1

Read the answers first. Then write the questions. Use the words in parentheses and any other necessary words. Put the verb in an appropriate tense.

Questions	**Answers**
1. (you / wait for) _Who are you waiting for?_	No one. I'm just waiting for the bus.
2. (you / not / want / to go swimming) _Don't you want to go swimming?_	No. It's too cold out.
3. (you / have / this car) _____	Since 1998.
4. (you / not / go / to work yesterday) _____	Because I was sick.
5. (the children / listen to) _____	A new CD. Should I ask them to turn the music down?*
6. (you / get up / tomorrow) _____	At 7:00, as usual.
7. (I / can / find / a good used car) _____	By looking in the newspaper. There are a lot for sale.
8. (you / not / feel / well) _____	Yes, I am. Why do you ask?
9. (your brother / do) _____	He's writing a letter.
10. (you / come / to this country) _____	Three years ago.
11. (you / meet / your husband) _____	A friend introduced us to each other.
12. (your teacher / not / born / in this country) _____	No, but she's a native speaker.
13. (these clothes / made) _____	In China, I think. Look at the labels.*
14. (wait / to see / me) _____	It's a gentleman, but I didn't get his name.

*turn the music down: *make the music less loud*   *label: *a piece of cloth on clothing showing the size, what the clothing is made of, instructions for cleaning, etc.*

Questions 2 (**Do you know where . . . ?** / **He asked me where . . .**)

Complete each conversation using the words in parentheses with a question word, *if*, or *whether*. Read B's answer first.

1. *A:* (that blue car / cost) Can you tell me ___how much that blue car costs___ ?
   B: It's $7,500.

2. *A:* (the magazines and newspapers / be) I wonder if you could tell me _____
   _____ ?
   B: They're on the second floor.

3. *A:* (that chicken / weigh) Could you tell me _____ ?
   B: It weighs just over three pounds.

4. *A:* (San Francisco / be) Do you have any idea _____
   _____ an expensive city?
   B: Yes, it's expensive but very nice.

5. *A:* (Shakespeare / be born) Do you remember _____ ?
   B: In 1564. And he died in 1616.

6. *A:* (you / get / angry) I can't understand _____
   at me yesterday.
   B: Because you hurt my feelings!

7. *A:* ("diffident" / mean) Do you happen to know _____ ?
   B: Yes, it means "shy."

8. *A:* (Ashgabat / be) I have absolutely no idea _____ .
   B: It's in Turkmenistan near the Caspian Sea.

9. *A:* (I / sent) Do you have any idea _____ to prison?
   B: No, I think they'll find you innocent.

10. *A:* (my car keys / be) I don't suppose you know _____ .
    B: Yes, I saw them on the hall table.

11. *A:* (a cell phone / cost) I'm not buying my 10-year-old son a phone! Do you know
    _____ ?
    B: They've gotten very cheap, Dad. Look on the Internet.

12. *A:* (the next movie / be) Can you tell me _____ ?
    B: Yes, it's at 9:30. Would you like a ticket?

13. *A:* (Matt / accept / the new job) Do you know _____ ?
    B: I don't think he did. He likes his present job.

Questions and Auxiliary Verbs

Questions 2 (Do you know where . . . ? / He asked me where . . .)

Write what the first person in each pair asked the second person. Use the questions and reported speech.

Can I see your driver's license?

Have you ever been to Hawaii?

Where do you have pain?

What time does the bus leave for the airport?

When are you going to hand in your homework?

1. (a police officer / me) _A police officer asked me whether (if) he could see my_
   driver's license.

2. (the teacher / Laura) The teacher asked Laura _____
   _____

3. (the doctor / me) _____
   _____

4. (we / the hotel clerk) _____
   _____

5. (the travel agent / Mrs. White) _____
   _____

Are we going to have a party in December?

Do I look good in my new dress?

How's the weather there?

Will it hurt very much?

Why can't I have my own cell phone?

6. (the patient / the dentist) _____
   _____

7. (I / my friend in Florida) _____
   _____

8. (Sally / her friend)_____
   _____

9. (the students / the teacher) _____
   _____

10. (Barbara / her father) _____
    _____

Auxiliary Verbs (**have/do/can**, etc.); **I think so / I hope so**, etc.

A. Complete the sentences. Use the words in parentheses. Look at the second part of the sentence carefully.

1. (olives / be / sweet) *Olives aren't sweet* , and neither are lemons.

2. (my brother / speak / Chinese) *My brother speaks Chinese* , but his wife doesn't.

3. (I / very quiet) *I am very quiet* , and so are my neighbors.

4. (I / see / the new hospital) _____
   _____ , and neither has Ron.

5. (I / have / more cake) _____
   _____ , and neither should you.

6. (Rex / like / to cook) _____ , and so does his wife.

7. (Sue / buy / Liz a present) _____
   _____ , but I did .

8. (Jeff / have to / leave / town) _____ ,
   _____ , and so did his brother.

9. (my boss / be / on vacation) _____ ,
   and so is his assistant.

B. Complete the second part of the sentence. Use the words in parentheses.

1. I can miss a day of work, and so *can you* (you).

2. Chris won't be at the party, but _____ (his girlfriend).

3. Sylvia hasn't been to Brazil, and neither _____ (I).

4. I should have left a tip, and so _____ (you).

5. Lou and Jessica are thinking of moving, and so _____ (Lou's sister).

6. I spend too much time on the computer, and so _____ (you).

7. The Carlsons couldn't reach their son on the phone, and neither _____ (I).

8. I didn't have to renew my driver's license, but _____ (my brother).

9. I wouldn't do such a thing, and neither _____
   (any friend of mine).

Questions and Auxiliary Verbs

Auxiliary verbs (**have/do/can**, etc.); **I think so / I hope so**, etc.

You're talking to a friend. Write true responses about yourself. If appropriate, use *so* or *neither* and the correct auxiliary verb. Look at the examples carefully.

Friend	**You**
1. I'd like something to eat.	_You would? So would I._
2. I'm too tired to go out tonight.	_You are? I'm not._
3. I didn't have time to read the paper yesterday.	_You didn't? Neither did I._
4. I would like to go to Moscow.	_____
5. My sister likes chocolate a lot.	_____
6. I have never been to India.	_____
7. Mrs. Smith didn't eat dinner last night.	_____
8. I can't play a musical instrument.	_____
9. I was very hungry when I got up this morning.	_____
10. I'm not going to take any trips this month.	_____
11. I should sleep more.	_____
12. My brother has to go to summer school.*	_____
13. I watched a very interesting program on TV last night.	_____
14. I wasn't born in this country.	_____
15. I wouldn't like to live in a foreign country.	_____
16. I'm going out for dinner tonight.	_____
17. I don't like hot weather very much.	_____
18. I haven't been to the dentist for ages.	_____
19. I am thinking of seeing a movie tonight.	_____
20. I try to do exercises every day.	_____

*summer school: *classes that take place during summer vacation*

Auxiliary verbs (**have/do/can**, etc.); **I think so / I hope so**, etc.

You are person B. Read the situation and A's question. Then write your answer using the word in parentheses and *so* or *not*.

1. You don't like fish.
   A: Is Ted cooking fish for dinner?
   B: (hope) ___I hope not.___

2. You are pretty sure the movie lasts only ninety minutes.
   A: The movie starts at 7:00 p.m. Will we be out by 9:00?
   B: (think) _____

3. Mark is usually off on Fridays.
   A: Is Mark working this Friday?
   B: (think) _____

4. Your electric bill is due today.
   A: Do we have to pay the electric bill today?
   B: (afraid) _____

5. You have very little extra money.
   A: Do you think I could borrow $20 till next week?
   B: (afraid) _____

6. You don't have any plans for Thursday night.
   A: Will you be home Thursday night?
   B: (guess) _____

7. The party started at 9:00 p.m., it's 11:30 p.m. now, and Alan hasn't come.
   A: Isn't Alan coming?
   B: (guess) _____

8. You already have plans for Friday night.
   A: Can you come over for dinner on Friday?
   B: (afraid) _____

9. The last time you checked, there was no sugar.
   A: Do we have any sugar?
   B: (think) _____

10. You don't like Matthew's cousin.
    A: Is Matthew bringing his cousin when he comes to see us?
    B: (hope) _____

11. Marge goes to church every Sunday.
    A: Do you think we'll see Marge in church?
    B: (suppose) _____

12. Jack doesn't have much money this year.
    A: Do you think Jack will take a long vacation this year?
    B: (suppose) _____

13. You love Chinese food.
    A: Are your parents taking us out for Chinese food?
    B: (hope) _____

14. Jack's in the hospital. He just had a serious operation.
    A: Will he be able to go home soon?
    B: (think) _____

15. Taxes always seem to go up, never down.
    A: Do you think taxes will go up again?
    B: (expect) _____

16. You're pretty sure Sue told you she's going to visit you tonight.
    A: Is Sue stopping by tonight?
    B: (think) _____

UNIT
50

Add question tags (*do you? isn't it?* etc.) to these statements to make them tag questions.

1. The mail carrier* is late today, _isn't he_ ?   Yes, a little.

2. You wouldn't lend Zachary $100, _would you_ ?   Not in a million years.

3. You can give me a hand* tomorrow, _____ ?   Yes, count on me.

4. There's something you're not telling me, _____ ?   No, I've told you every detail.

5. Cheese should be kept in the refrigerator, _____ ?   Yes, it should.

6. I'm not wearing two different socks, _____ ?   Yes, but no one will notice.

7. Let me think about that question for a minute, _____ ?   Yes, of course.

8. Matthew said he was coming to the party, _____ ?   Yes, he did.

9. Let's give him a call to make sure he's coming, _____ ?   If you want to.

10. Alison won't forget to bring the CDs, _____ ?   I hope not.

11. We don't have much time, _____ ?   No, we certainly don't.

12. You wouldn't have an extra dollar or two, _____ ?   No, I'm broke.* Sorry.

13. There hasn't been an accident on the freeway, _____ ?   Not that I know of.

14. We haven't forgotten anything, _____ ?   I don't think so. I'll check.

15. A cell phone would be cheaper than a land line, _____ ?   I'm not sure it would be.

16. Your sister wishes she was married, _____ ?   Not really.

17. Let's stay cool and calm, _____ ?   I'm too angry to be calm.

18. Your friends won't be upset if we're a little late, _____ ? No, but let's hurry anyway.

19. The Nelsons spend a lot of time away from home, _____ ?   Yes, they travel a lot.

20. I'm an easy person to get along with, _____ ?   Well, if you say so.

*mail carrier: *person who delivers mail (letters, postcards, packages) to a home or business*   *give someone a hand: *to help someone*   *broke: *without money*

Auxiliary verbs (**have/do/can**, etc.); Tag Questions (**do you?** / **isn't it?**, etc.)

Respond to these questions and statements with your own answers. Respond with *yes/no* and auxiliaries.

1. You can speak English quite well, can't you?

   Yes, I can. (OR No, I can't.)

2. War is sometimes necessary.

   Yes, it is. (OR No, it isn't. OR No, it never is.)

3. Are you a teenager?

   Yes, I am. (OR No, I'm not anymore. OR No, I'm an adult now.)

4. You haven't been to Antarctica, have you? _____

5. Material possessions* are very important. _____

6. Education changes people in many ways. _____

7. The cost of living has gone up a lot recently. _____

8. Rich people have an obligation to help poor people, don't they? _____

9. We should all try to help people who are less fortunate than we are. _____

10. Are you a parent? _____

11. Women with children should be able to work if they want to. _____

12. Fathers can take care of children as well as mothers can. _____

13. The weather has a big effect on people. _____

14. You don't like rainy days better than sunny ones, do you? _____

15. Aren't you glad that you study English? _____

16. The world would be a better place if everyone spoke the same language. _____

17. There has been a decrease in the number of languages in the world, hasn't there? _____

*material possessions: *things we own like clothes, furniture, and cars*

Questions and Auxiliary Verbs

Questions and Auxiliary Verbs

Think of a person you want to meet. Write eight questions to ask that person. Include at least two tag questions and at least two questions that begin with _Do you know . . . ?_ or _Can you tell me . . . ?_

Name of Person: _Meryl Streep_

1. _How many movies have you been in?_
2. _You still practice your lines a lot, don't you?_
3. _Can you tell me if you plan to make any new movies next year?_

Name of Person: _____

1. _____
2. _____
3. _____
4. _____
5. _____
6. _____
7. _____
8. _____

What questions do you wish people would ask you?

1. _Do you like living with your family?_
2. _Can you tell me what the most important thing in life is to you?_
3. _____
4. _____
5. _____
6. _____
7. _____
8. _____

Verb + -ing (enjoy doing / stop doing, etc.)

Complete the sentences, keeping the same meaning. Use *-ing*.

1. The Petersons like to eat out.

    The Petersons enjoy _eating out_ .

2. Don't interrupt me again, please.

    Would you please stop _____ me?

3. I can't work in that office anymore.

    I can't go on _____
    _____ office.

4. Does it bother you to live alone?

    Do you mind _____ ?

5. Luke isn't going to change jobs until next year.

    Luke is going to put off _____
    _____ until next year.

6. We have to do the shopping first; then we can go home.

    We can't go home until we finish _____
    _____ .

7. Louise said, "Why don't we watch a video at home?"

    Louise suggested _____
    _____ at home.

8. Why does Josh tell the same stories about his dog again and again?

    Why does Josh keep _____
    _____ his dog?

9. I'm not going to try to change my husband's bad habits anymore.

    I've given up _____
    _____ .

10. Greg can't lift anything heavy until his back is better.

    Greg has to avoid _____
    _____ until his back is better.

11. I used to walk to work every day, and I miss it now.

    I miss _____ day.

12. I'm sorry I talked about you behind your back.

    I regret _____
    _____ behind your back.

13. It's not even a possibility for me to live in a different country from my parents!

    I would never consider _____
    _____ from my parents!

14. Don't cheat; you might get caught.

    You risk _____ if you cheat.

15. How would it be to live without music?

    Can you imagine _____
    _____ ?

16. The robber says he broke into the house but didn't steal anything.

    The robber admits _____
    _____

    but denies _____ .

Complete the sentences for these situations.

Did you remember to mail my package?

No, I didn't. Sorry.

1. _He_ forgot _to mail her package_ .

Did you finally get a raise at work?

Yes, I finally did. I kept asking for a raise until I got one.

2. _____ finally managed _____ .

It really hurts me when you call me stupid.

I'm sorry. I won't do it again.

3. _____ promised _____ .

Can I give you a ride home?

That's all right. I have my car.

4. _____ offered _____ .

Can you stay late to finish the report?

No problem. I'll stay until it's done.

5. _____ agreed _____ .

Are you going to visit your family this Christmas?

No, I don't have enough money.

6. _____ can't afford _____ .

EXERCISE CONTINUES ▶▶

Should we buy a new car?

I guess you're right.

No, I don't think that's a good idea right now.

7. They decided _____ .

Josh, if you don't get a haircut, I will keep you in the house until you do.

Are you serious?!

8. _____ threatened _____ if he
_____ .

Mom, can you give me five dollars?

No, you haven't done your chores.*

I don't know what you mean.

I mean you haven't earned your allowance.*

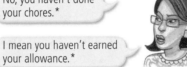

9. She refused _____ .

He pretended _____ .

Can I get the afternoon off?

I will.

I don't see why not if you finish all your work this morning.

10. _____ arranged _____ .

How can I get to the airport from here?

Take Route 280 south to 101 north, and get off at Coleman. Then follow the signs.

11. _____ explained to her _____ .

*chore: *a household job that has to be done regularly, such as washing dishes or taking garbage outside*
*allowance: *money that parents give children regularly, usually for doing chores*

-ing and the Infinitive

Verb + (Object) + **to** . . . (I want you **to** . . . , etc.)

Complete the sentences, keeping the same meaning.

1. "Please, please let me go with you,"
   Sean said to us.

   Sean begged _to go with us_ .

2. They said I could have a key to the
   building.

   They let _me have a key to the building_ .

3. Shall I lock the car?

   Would you like _me to lock the car_ ?

4. Do you think it would be a good idea
   for Rob to get a job?

   Would you advise _____
   _____ ?

5. Were you surprised your company
   fired* so many people?

   Did you expect _____
   _____ ?

6. How did you learn to play the piano?

   Who taught _____ ?

7. My parents think I should become a
   doctor.

   My parents want _____
   _____ .

8. You can't smoke in this building.

   You aren't allowed _____
   _____ .

9. What did you do to make the baby
   stop crying?

   How did you get _____
   _____ ?

10. I didn't break your glasses on purpose.

    I didn't mean _____ .

11. Mike's suggestion was useless to
    me in making my decision.

    Mike's suggestion didn't help _____
    _____ .

12. "Never use anyone else's computer,"
    the director told me very clearly.

    I was ordered _____
    _____ .

13. Do I need to pay for the book I lost?

    Do you want _____
    _____ ?

14. I have been told I absolutely shouldn't
    give my credit card number to a
    stranger on the phone.

    I have been warned _____
    _____ .

15. I was made to leave the theater to use
    my cell phone.

    They made _____
    _____ .

16. You look slim in that black suit.

    That black suit makes _____
    _____ .

fire: to tell somebody they don't have a job anymore

-ing and the Infinitive

Verb + **-ing** or **to** . . . 1 (**remember/regret**, etc.);
Verb + **-ing** or **to** . . . 2 (**try/need/help**)

EXERCISE
78

Complete the sentences with verb + -ing or to + verb. Use an appropriate verb.

UNITS
54–55

1. After getting a degree in history, Susan went on __*to study*__ journalism at another university.

2. Max doesn't remember __*calling*__ the police, but I heard him make the call.

3. I should have bought my holiday presents sooner. I regret not _____ them when the stores were less crowded.

4. I couldn't help _____ when I saw Ted. I always think of the funny joke he told us.

5. Mrs. Brown said she would go on _____ at the library until she retired.

6. The stain* on my shirt is gone. I tried _____ lemon juice on the stain, and it worked.

7. Before I leave town, I have to remember _____ my suit from the cleaner's.

8. If one aspirin doesn't help your toothache, try _____ two aspirins every four hours.

9. I am starting _____ a little better now with the new medicine I'm taking.

10. Don't you remember _____ my boss at our party last year? She was the one who kept asking you questions about computers.

11. My doctor told me I need _____ a lot of juice and tea until my cold is better.

12. You are very upset because of the accident. Try _____ calm when you talk to the police.

13. Our history teacher discussed the American Revolution. Then he went on _____ the American Civil War with us.

14. Can someone help me _____ the groceries into the house from the car?

15. *(in a letter)* We regret _____ you that your application was received too late to be considered for the position.

16. Why does Jon keep _____ Sally to go out with him? She never accepts.

17. My suit will need _____ before the wedding next week. It's dirty.

18. I remember _____ my credit card to the waiter at the restaurant last night, but I don't remember _____ it back from him.

19. Marge has had a very hard life. I can't help _____ sorry for her.

*stain: a dirty mark, usually on clothing, that is difficult to remove

Verb **-ing** or **to . . .** 2 (**try/need/help**);
Verb **-ing** or **to . . .** 3 (**like / would like**, etc.)

Choose the correct completion for each sentence.

1. I'm so tired of my job. I'd really love __b__ a month off from work.
   a. taking   b. to take   c. take

2. Are you a morning person? Do you like _____ early even when you don't have to?
   a. to get up   b. get up   c. to have gotten up

3. I went shopping yesterday. Last night my parents told me they would like _____ with me.
   a. going   b. to go   c. to have gone

4. My parents said they don't like _____ home alone when I go out.
   a. to leave   b. leaving   c. to be left

5. "My husband complains about everything. What should I do?" "Have you tried _____ him?
   a. ignore   b. to ignore   c. ignoring

6. I've tried _____ this lamp so many times, but it just won't work. I'm buying a new one.
   a. fix   b. to fix   c. fixing

7. Nicholas wishes he hadn't moved. He seems to hate _____ with his new roommate.
   a. living   b. to live   c. to have lived

8. You poor thing! I would hate _____ what you did.
   a. experiencing   b. having experienced   c. to have experienced

9. My sister is always telling me what to do. I would like her _____ less bossy.
   a. being   b. to be   c. to have been

10. Could you help me _____ for my car keys? I can't find them anywhere.
    a. looking   b. to have looked   c. look

11. Life is just sad sometimes. Most people can't help _____ unhappy once in a while.*
    a. feeling   b. to feel   c. to have felt

12. I'm not ready to make a decision yet. Does anyone else think the matter needs _____ some more?
    a. to discuss   b. to have discussed   c. to be discussed

13. I have never needed _____ the battery in my cell phone.
    a. changing   b. to change   c. to have changed

14. Please believe me. I honestly don't mind _____ for you if you won't be long.
    a. to wait   b. wait   c. waiting

*once in a while: *occasionally, sometimes*

Prefer and would rather

Complete the second sentence, using the words in parentheses and other necessary words.

1. Robbie doesn't like hot tea. (have iced tea / hot tea) He'd rather _have iced tea_
   than hot tea . (iced tea / hot tea) He prefers _iced tea to hot tea_ .

2. Fred likes staying on his boat. (stay on his boat / live in a house) He prefers _staying on_
   his boat to living in a house .

3. Are you going to make dinner? (I / make it) Or would you rather I _made it_ ?

4. I like working at home. (work at home / in an office) I'd much rather _____
   _____ .

5. Don't you feel like going out tonight? (you / stay) _____ rather
   _____ home?

6. Chris doesn't want to go to Las Vegas on vacation. (Puerto Rico / Las Vegas) She prefers
   _____ .

7. Will you phone George? (call him) Or would you rather I _____ ?

8. Your German is better than mine. (translate the letter) I'd rather you _____
   _____ .

9. I don't like going to the movies. (watch a movie at home / go out) I prefer _____
   _____ .

10. I don't like eating in restaurants. (eat at home / in a restaurant) I'd rather we _____
    _____ .

11. I don't want to delay doing my report. (do it now / later) I would prefer _____
    _____ .

12. "Do you feel like going dancing tonight?" (not do) "No, I'm tired; I _____
    rather _____ anything that requires so much energy."

13. "Are you going to my cousin's wedding with me?" (go by yourself) "No, I'd rather you
    _____ , if you don't mind."

14. Are you a very sociable person? (go to a party / read a book) Do you prefer _____
    _____ ?

15. My brother is a computer nerd.* (chat on the Internet / talk to someone in person) He
    would rather _____ .

*computer nerd: *someone who really likes computers and uses them all the time*

-ing and the Infinitive

Preposition (in/for/about, etc.) + -ing

Complete the sentences, keeping the same meaning. Use a verb + *-ing*.

1. Let's not go to a restaurant. Let's cook something at home instead.
   Let's cook something at home instead of _going to a restaurant_ .

2. How does Andrew expect to do well in school? He doesn't make an effort.
   How does Andrew expect to do well in school without _____ ?

3. My teacher told me to improve my pronunciation. She said to listen to native speakers.
   My teacher told me to improve my pronunciation by _____ .

4. Ted brushes his teeth after he eats and before he goes to bed.
   Ted brushes his teeth after _____ and before _____ .

5. I'm going to have dinner at my favorite restaurant tonight. I'm excited.
   I am looking forward to _____ .

6. Pam runs five miles every day, and she is really tired of it.
   Pam is fed up with _____ .

7. The politician used public money for himself. Now he's in trouble.
   The politician got into trouble for _____ .

8. Hank is lonely because it's difficult for him to make friends.
   Hank is lonely because he isn't good at _____ .

9. We might go to Toronto next weekend. How does that sound to you?
   Are you interested in _____ ?

10. I found the restaurant, and nobody gave me directions.
    I found the restaurant without anybody _____ .

11. Sarah went to work this morning even though she had to drive on snow and ice.
    Sarah went to work this morning in spite of _____ .

12. Would you like to take a break and have a snack?
    How about _____ and _____ ?

13. You're going to see your brother. Are you happy about that?
    Are you looking forward to _____ ?

14. Jake didn't return his boss's phone calls. Now he's in trouble.
    Jake is in trouble for _____ .

15. We'll never get tickets for the game this late.
    We have no chance of _____ .

Be/get used to something (I'm used to . . .)

A. Read the passage about Alice's first year at college. Put the verbs in parentheses in the correct form.

When Alice first went away to college last September, she wasn't used to 1) _taking_ (take) care of herself. It was the first time she had lived away from her parents, so she was very homesick in the beginning. At home, she used to 2) _have_ (have) her own room, so she wasn't used to 3) _____ (share) an apartment with another person at first. It took her a few months to get used to 4) _____ (live) with her college roommate.

When she was in high school, her parents used to 5) _____ (remind) her to do her homework and 6) _____ (make) decisions for her. In college, she had to get used to 7) _____ (be) more independent. No one reminds her to study, and she has to make her own decisions. Her high school classes were easy. In college, she had to get used to 8) _____ (study) very hard – two hours or more for every hour of class.

In high school, Alice used to 9) _____ (drive) her parents' car when she needed to go somewhere. In college, she is now used to 10) _____ (ride) a bike and 11) _____ (take) the bus. At home, Alice's mother used to 12) _____ (do) all the shopping, cooking, and cleaning. Alice didn't use to 13) _____ (help) out much. At college, she had to get used to 14) _____ (be) more responsible.

B. Complete the sentences with an appropriate form of *be used to*, *get used to*, or *used to*.

1. If you travel a lot, meals can be a problem unless you _are used to_ eating different kinds of food.

2. They say Sam never goes to the gym anymore, but he _____ exercise all the time when I knew him.

3. A new job can be stressful unless you are good at _____ new situations and new people.

4. I don't have a car anymore, but I _____ have one.

5. I had a terrible time when I started working nights. I had to _____ sleeping during the day instead of at night.

6. At first, Sarah couldn't fall asleep in her new apartment because she _____ living so close to a big, noisy highway.

7. This soup may taste strange to you if you _____ eating fish.

-ing and the Infinitive

Verb + Preposition + -ing (succeed in -ing / accuse somebody of -ing, etc.)

Complete the sentences. Use the correct preposition and an appropriate verb + -ing. Some sentences require an object pronoun (*me*, *him*, *them*, etc.) and some require *not*.

1. I've been thinking __*of buying*__ a new TV, but I don't know where to buy it.

2. Ann accused __*me of lying* (OR *me of not telling the truth)*__ , but I swear* I told her the truth.

3. Do you feel _____ to a movie, or would you rather stay home?

4. I wouldn't dream _____ your car without asking you first.

5. Excuse _____ here on time. I had trouble with my car again.

6. I think we should apologize _____ your brother's birthday. We didn't remember to call or send a card.

7. I'm not looking forward _____ my speech in front of class next week. I always get nervous.

8. When I travel with Ben, he always insists _____ at the best hotels.

9. I hope you succeed _____ a nice apartment. I know you've been looking for one for a long time.

10. What prevented the fire department _____ to the fire more quickly? It took the fire truck almost 20 minutes to get there.

11. My daughter is 18, so I can't stop _____ her friends even if I don't like them.

12. I am thinking _____ to Argentina. Have you ever been there?

13. Do those children watch too much TV? Do you think the TV keeps _____ _____ their homework?

14. I'd like to congratulate you _____ promoted to manager in your company.

15. Sarah is the most honest person I know. How can you accuse _____ dishonest?

16. It's hard for me to trust Max to tell the truth anymore. I suspect _____ _____ to me every time we speak.

17. We decided not to go to Cal's wedding. I don't think Cal will ever forgive _____ _____ .

18. Tom just lost his job, so he decided _____ a new car at this time.

*swear: *to promise very seriously to tell the truth*

Expressions + -ing

Complete the sentences, keeping the same meaning. Use -ing.

1. There's nothing you can do about your brother's divorce. Don't worry about it.

   It's no use _worrying about your_ _brother's divorce_ .

2. I liked the movie and think others should see it too.

   That movie is worth _seeing_ .

3. It's not easy for Ted to apologize to people.

   Ted has difficulty _____ _____ .

4. I wouldn't keep this old magazine.

   There's no point in _____ old magazine.

5. There's nothing good on TV. Why watch it?

   What's the point of _____ _____ when there's nothing good on?

6. Should we walk all the way to the market just to buy lemons?

   Is it worth _____ _____ just to buy lemons?

7. Don't bother calling Mary Jo. She won't answer the phone.

   It's no use _____ because she won't answer the phone.

8. It was very hard for me to contact my uncle.

   I had a problem _____ _____ .

9. Margie shops too much.

   Margie goes _____ too often.

10. Don't bother inviting Emily to the party. She won't be in town then.

    There's no point in _____ to the party because she will be out of town then.

11. Lee worked on his car from 8:00 a.m. till 3:00 p.m. yesterday.

    Lee spent seven hours _____ _____ yesterday.

12. For exercise, Sam skis in the winter and swims in the summer.

    For exercise, Sam goes _____ _____ _____ .

13. Is it hard to read without glasses?

    Do you have trouble _____ _____ ?

14. I think it's foolish to buy bottled water.

    I think you're wasting your money _____ _____ .

15. Why drive 50 miles to try to catch fish? There are no more fish in the lake.

    What's the point of _____ to go _____ in an empty lake?

-ing and the Infinitive

-ing and the Infinitive

Complete the passages with the verbs in parentheses in the correct form: verb + _-ing_, _to_ + verb, or base form.

A

A friend of mine, Judy, is thinking of 1) ___working___ (work) abroad for two years. She hasn't decided whether 2) ___to look___ (look) for a job in Asia or in South America. She has always wanted 3) _____ (visit) both places. Judy regrets not 4) _____ (take) a foreign language in college, and she hopes that it will not prevent her from 5) _____ (get) a job in another country. A friend advised her 6) _____ (decide) where she would like 7) _____ (go) first. Then she can learn as much of the language of the country as possible before 8) _____ (leave) on her trip. There's no point in 9) _____ (study) Chinese if she goes to Chile, is there? She needs 10) _____ (know) where she is going to move before she learns a language. She is a physical therapist,* so of course, she can't expect 11) _____ (help) patients if she doesn't speak their language.

Judy is a flexible,* intelligent person. I don't think she will have trouble 12) _____ (get) used to life in another country. I have to say that I can't help 13) _____ (feel) a little jealous of her. I would love 14) _____ (live) abroad, too, but I would rather 15) _____ (go) to the Middle East. I have dreamed of 16) _____ (visit) Egypt and Turkey since I was little. I can't leave my job now, though. I will have to put off 17) _____ (travel) for at least three years.

B

Valerie Lim persuaded her parents to let her 1) _____ (have) a party for her birthday. Val is really looking forward to 2) _____ (turn) 12 and to 3) _____ (feel) special on that day. Her parents would rather 4) _____ (give) the party at home than in a restaurant, as many families do. They are planning 5) _____ (invite) Val's classmates, relatives, and family friends. They will have to spend a lot of time 6) _____ (buy and prepare) food for the party, but everyone will appreciate 7) _____ (eat) home cooking more than restaurant food. They are used to 8) _____ (celebrate) family events at home. They know they can count on relatives and friends to help 9) _____ (get) ready for the party. The Lims have told people 10) _____ (not / bring) birthday presents. They want to make their guests 11) _____ (feel) welcome and, of course, they want their daughter 12) _____ (remember) this birthday as a special one.

*physical therapist: _a person who is trained to use exercises, massage, etc., to treat injuries_   *flexible: _able to change to fit different situations_

To . . . , for . . . , and **so that** . . . (Purpose)

Read the questions. Write short answers using the words in parentheses. Use *for*, *to*, or *so that*.

1. Why did Josh go to the store? (some milk) _For some milk._
   (get some milk / us) _To get some milk for us._
   (could buy milk) _So that he could buy some milk._

2. What did Sheila want? (money / pay her tuition) _Money to pay her tuition._

3. What did you sit down for? (try on some shoes) _____

4. Why did you take Colin downtown? (his driving test) _____

5. What are we stopping for? (have some lunch) _____

6. Why did Sandy write a note to herself? (wouldn't forget to stop at the bank)

   _____

7. What did you give Tim $30 for? (could buy groceries) _____

8. What does the new job offer you? (the opportunity / make more money)

   _____

9. Why did they close the store early? (could spend the holiday with family)

   _____

10. Why does Seth wear that wool scarf? (keep his neck warm) _____

11. Why did Josh's grandmother give him so much money? (could go to college)

    _____

12. Why do you want to go to the mountains? (a change) _____

13. Why are you leaving so early? (won't miss my bus) _____

14. What is Stan saving his money for? (a trip to Finland) _____

15. What do you need to improve your English? (the opportunity / talk to people)

    _____

16. Why did the director close the door to her office? (some privacy*) _____

17. Why does our son close his bedroom door? (keep us out) _____

18. Why does Frank act so unfriendly? (keep people away) _____

19. Why are you standing in line? (can buy some stamps) _____

20. Why does Mr. Simms go fishing so often? (relaxation) _____

*privacy: *situation in which no one disturbs you*

-ing and the Infinitive

Adjective + to . . .

What do you say in these situations? Read the situation and complete the sentence with an infinitive. Sometimes you need to include *of* + pronoun.

1. You heard your friend's father had an accident. You say to your friend:
   I was sorry _to hear (that) your father had an accident_ .

2. Your classmate Yuko spent two hours helping you with your homework. You say to her:
   It was considerate _of you to help me with my homework_ .

3. You saw your friend Rachel on TV. You say to her:
   I was surprised _____ .

4. You heard that your friend Mike got out of the hospital. You say to another friend:
   I was relieved _____ .

5. You found out you didn't get the job you applied for. You say to a friend:
   I was very disappointed _____ .

6. You met your friend's parents the other night. You say to your friend:
   I was very glad _____ .

7. Carlos often goes to bed with the doors unlocked. You say to him:
   It is careless _____ .

8. It hasn't rained for a month, but clouds are building. You say to your father:
   Look at those clouds. It's bound _____ soon.

9. Andy quit his job before finding another one. You say to him:
   It was foolish _____ .

10. No one except you got the right answer. You say to your parents:
    I was the only one _____ .

11. Your parents are punishing your sister for something she didn't do. You say to a friend:
    It's unfair _____ .

12. Milo has a heavy accent, and you can't understand him. You say to another classmate:
    It's difficult _____ .

13. Jason is such a careless driver. He'll probably have an accident. You say to him:
    You're likely* _____ if you're not more careful.

14. Maria offered the police officer money not to give her a speeding ticket.* You say to another friend:
    It was foolish _____ .

*likely: *probable*   *speeding ticket: *a note saying you have to pay money for driving too fast*

To . . . (afraid to do) and Preposition + -ing (afraid of -ing)

Complete the conversation between the director of a language school and her new, inexperienced assistant, Laura. Use the verbs in parentheses in the appropriate form. Add prepositions where necessary.

Laura: I'm sorry 1) <u>to interrupt</u> (interrupt) your meeting, but someone would like

2) _____ (talk) to you on the phone, Ms. Garcia. The gentleman is

interested 3) _____ (learn) more about our language school and

what books we use. He called yesterday, but I failed 4) _____ (give)

you the message. I'm so sorry 5) _____ (forget). I was hoping

6) _____ (have) a word with you right after lunch, but I was afraid

7) _____ (make) you angry because I heard you talking on the

phone. I was thinking 8) _____ (ask) the man on the phone for his

name. But then I received another call, so I asked him to wait. Unfortunately, he had

hung up* when I went back to him, so I didn't succeed 9) _____

(get) his name. Then I had an emergency at home that prevented me

10) _____ (be) here the rest of the afternoon.

Director: I'm sorry your first day was so hard, Laura. Don't be so polite that it stops you

11) _____ (do) your job. When you find out what his name is,

I'll probably know whether I need to speak to him or not. Meanwhile, tell him that

I look forward 12) _____ (speak) with him very soon. And tell him

that I am extremely sorry 13) _____ (not / be) able to take his call

at this time.

Laura: Yes, ma'am. Sorry 14) _____ (do) everything wrong.

Director: Don't worry. I'm sure you will be interested 15) _____ (know) one

very important rule I have: You are always allowed 16) _____

(interrupt) me for something important, but I never want you

17) _____ (waste) my time on unimportant matters. Is that clear?

Laura: I would never dream 19) _____ (waste) your time, Ms. Garcia.

Follow-up: Think of a time when your inexperience kept you from doing the right thing. What did you fail to do or not succeed in doing? What were you sorry for doing? Write about it on a separate piece of paper.

hang up: end a telephone conversation

-ing and the Infinitive

See somebody do and see somebody doing

Complete the sentences. Use an appropriate verb.

1. A lot of people say Gloria is a gossip,* but I haven't actually heard her __*say*__ anything bad about anybody.

2. On the way home from work, I saw my neighbor Fred __*cutting*__ his grass in the rain.

3. I'm not good with children. It breaks my heart to listen to them _____ .

4. I didn't actually see Helen _____ , but they say she fell and hurt herself at the factory yesterday.

5. Listen. Can you hear air _____ from this tire?

6. When I was leaving home this morning, I noticed a stranger _____ on my neighbor's door.

7. That's a terrible word for a child to use. I never want to hear you _____ it again.

8. Kevin got angry at his sister because he found her _____ his new sweater.

9. Ted can't be very sick. Some friends saw him _____ in a restaurant last night.

10. Why do you think it was Sam who told Jane your secret? Did you see him _____ to her?

11. Could you look out the window and tell me if you see a taxi _____ ? I called one 20 minutes ago.

12. Fred is a very patient person. I've never seen him _____ his temper.

13. When I got home, I could smell food _____ on the stove. It made me hungry.

14. As I was leaving the doctor's office, I heard the doctor and nurse _____ about my case.

15. The suspect* was last seen _____ a large black truck.

16. I slept through the earthquake last night, so I didn't actually feel the house _____ .

17. I looked up because I thought I heard someone _____ my name.

18. Guess who I saw _____ meat at the supermarket. Our vegetarian friend, Carol!

19. If you have a chance to listen to Andrew _____ the guitar, you'll find out what a good musician he is.

20. A witness is a person who sees an event _____ , especially a crime or an accident.

*gossip: *a person who likes to talk about other people*   *suspect: *a person believed to have committed a crime*

-ing Phrases (Feeling tired, I went to bed early.)

Write the story in paragraph form. Join each pair of sentences by making the italicized one an *-ing* phrase.

I hurt my arm. / *I helped a friend fix his car yesterday.*

I went to the doctor. / *I hoped that she could relieve* the pain.*

I had arrived late in the day without an appointment. / I had to wait to see the doctor.

I had to wait a long time. / *I sat in an uncomfortable chair.*

The doctor gave me a prescription* for a painkiller.* / *She promised it would work fast.*

I didn't know that they would upset my stomach. / I took the pills without food.

He had left me at the doctor's earlier. / My friend came to my house to see me last night.

I woke up this morning. / *I felt a little better.*

I called work to say I wasn't going in. / I ate and went back to bed.

I hurt my arm helping a friend fix his car yesterday. I went to the doctor hoping

that she could relieve the pain. Having arrived late in the day without an

appointment, I had to wait to see the doctor.

_____

_____

_____

_____

_____

_____

_____

_____

---

*relieve: *to make less bad*   *prescription: *a doctor's instruction saying a pharmacist is allowed to sell you specific medication*   *painkiller: *pill that reduces pain*

-ing and the Infinitive

Complete the sentences, keeping the same meaning.

1. We can't wait to go to Alaska next summer.
   We're looking forward _to going to Alaska next summer_____ .

2. I bet you're sorry you didn't buy a house when prices were low.
   I bet you regret _____ .

3. It's a shame we couldn't come to your party.
   We would like _____ .

4. Should I put the dishes away?
   Do you want _____ ?

5. Sheila has no intention of getting married.
   Sheila doesn't intend _____ .

6. There is no way I could ask for another day off.
   I wouldn't dream _____ .

7. We wanted to turn around and drive the other way, but the police wouldn't let us.
   The police stopped _____ .

8. I'm not going to try to be friends with Pat any more.
   I give up _____ .

9. "I swear I didn't tell anyone your secret," Tim said.
   Tim denied _____ .

10. Shirley saw me but acted as if she hadn't.
    Shirley pretended _____ .

11. No one knew that we left a present for Bob.
    We left a present for Bob without _____ .

12. "You lied to me," Claudia said to her boyfriend.
    Claudia accused _____ .

13. My grandfather can't see well without glasses.
    My grandfather has trouble _____ .

14. I know you ate the last cookie.
    I saw you _____ .

-ing and the Infinitive

Answer the questions with your own words. Use *-ing* and the infinitive carefully.

1. Can you imagine living on another planet? Would you consider it if someone offered you the chance to go? Why or why not?

    I can't imagine living on another planet, and I wouldn't consider it if I were

    offered the chance to go. I am too attached to my family and friends here.

2. What have you arranged to do in the near future? _____
    _____

3. What have you been warned not to do by several people? _____
    _____

4. What pleasant things do you remember doing as a child? _____
    _____

5. What do you regret doing as a teenager? _____
    _____

6. What have you done before but won't go on doing now? _____
    _____

7. Think of a recent problem. What did you try doing to solve it? _____
    _____

8. What two things need to be done to make the world better? _____
    _____

9. What would you hate to see happen in the world? _____
    _____

10. Would you rather have a job working with a group of people or working alone? Why?
    _____

11. What is the last thing you thanked someone for? _____
    _____

12. If you went to live in a very cold climate, what would you have to get used to? _____
    _____

13. What have you done recently that you apologized to someone for doing? _____
    _____

14. What is one thing you would not forgive a person for doing? _____
    _____

-ing and the Infinitive

Use your own ideas to complete each sentence. Use an appropriate verb in the correct form: verb + *-ing*, *to* + verb, or the base form. Use any other words that you need.

1. On their next vacation, my friends are looking forward to *going to the Czech Republic* .
   On their next vacation, my friends are looking forward to _____ .

2. I am studying English *to get a better job* .
   I am studying English _____ .

3. Yesterday, I was surprised to hear *a young person use very rude language* .
   Yesterday, I was surprised to hear _____ .

4. When I go to a new place, it's never easy for me to get used to _____
   _____ .

5. I'm used to _____ ,
   but I will never get used to _____ .

6. At the end of a busy day, I sometimes feel like _____ .

7. I need to thank _____ for _____ .

8. Nothing can keep me from _____ .

9. A friend of mine spends a lot of time _____ .

10. When I have free time, I like to go _____ .

11. It is not thoughtful of people _____ .

12. When I was little, I was afraid _____ .

13. As for the future, I'm interested in _____ .

14. I have never seen anyone _____ .

15. One day I hope to hear _____ .

16. Not _____ ,
    I have trouble _____ .

17. After _____ ,
    I sometimes _____ .

18. While _____ ,
    I saw _____ .

Countable and Uncountable 1 & 2

Answer the questions using the words in the lists. Add *a/an* or the plural *-s* when necessary.

1. Which of these does a person need on a trip by car? Which doesn't a person need?
   airline ticket, gas, spare tire, tool, flashlight, suitcase, computer, map, time

   a. On a trip by car, a person needs <u>*gas, a spare tire, tools, a flashlight, suitcases*</u>
      <u>(OR *a suitcase), a map* (OR *maps), and time*</u> .

   b. A person doesn't need <u>*an airline ticket or a computer*</u> .

2. Which of these are good in a salad? Which aren't good?
   black pepper, butter, garlic, jam, lemon juice, lettuce, mushroom, oil, olive, piece of onion, banana, salt, tomato

   a. _____
      _____ are good in a salad.

   b. _____ aren't good in a salad.

3. Which of these are useful to a soccer player? Which are not useful?
   experience, good coach, strong arms and legs, healthy lungs, long hair, rainy weather, time to practice, umbrella

   a. _____
      _____ are useful to a soccer player.

   b. _____ are not useful.

4. Which of these do the parents of a new baby need? Which don't they need?
   baby clothes, good doctor, help from relatives, information about vaccinations,* money, truck, new living room furniture, spare room

   a. The parents of a new baby need _____
      _____ .

   b. They don't need _____ .

5. Which of these does a person need to be healthy? Which are not necessary for good health?
   alcohol, car, clean water, coffee, enough sleep, expensive doctor, exercise, fresh air, good food, hard job, stress, tobacco

   a. To be healthy, a person needs _____
      _____ .

   b. _____
      _____ are not necessary for good health.

6. What do you look for in a friend? What is not important?
   advice, dependability, funny personality, good behavior, good character, intelligence, person who knows how to listen, rich parents, similarity to you

   a. In a friend, I look for _____
      _____ .

   b. _____
      _____ are not important.

*vaccination: *protection against disease (e.g., polio) by an injection*

Complete the sentences. Use the words and phrases in the box. Sometimes you need *a/an* or the plural *-s*.

bad luck	bread	foreign travel	~~good news~~	helpful advice	~~job~~
luggage	permission	suggestion	trip	view	

1. I have __good news__ . My brother got __a job__ in Australia.

2. *(in a car)* Can I make _____ ? I think we should stop for gas.

3. Gloria gave me some _____ about selling my car.

4. Poor Frank. _____ seems to follow him.

5. You can't make a sandwich. We don't have any _____ .

6. In school, students must ask for _____ to leave the room.

7. Jan and Steve rented the apartment because it has _____ of the river.

8. Barbara bought some new _____ . She's taken two
_____ to Korea this year.

9. A passport is required for _____ .

behavior	big suitcase	experience	good progress	hair
hard work	information	room	room	unusual experience

10. Now that her children live on their own, Mrs. Philips rents _____
to three or four students.

11. The trunk of my car has _____ for two _____
_____ .

12. You're making _____ in math. It's because of your _____
_____ , I think.

13. Mr. Gomez is over 80, but he still has lots of nice white _____ .

14. Young Tommy's _____ has improved since his parents started
discussing problems more openly with him.

15 Do you have enough _____ to apply for that job?

16. The _____ I received about the party must have been wrong.
There's nobody here and the party was supposed to start an hour ago.

17. I had _____ the other day. A man mistook me for his boss.

Countable and Uncountable 1 & 2; Countable Nouns with **a/an** and **some**; **A/an** and **the**

Put in *a/an*, *the*, or *some*. Leave the space empty if none of these is possible.

There is a huge supermarket near my house called 1) _—_ Jones's Market. 2) _The_
supermarket is open 24 hours 3) _a_ day, seven days 4) _____ week, so I can shop
whenever I feel like it. When I go shopping for 5) _____ food, I usually take my cart
to 6) _____ produce section first because I eat a lot of fresh fruit and 7) _____
vegetables. I buy 8) _____ meat, but not very much. Yesterday, I bought 9) _____
whole chicken and 10) _____ pound of ground beef. I froze 11) _____ beef to use
later, but I'll cook 12) _____ chicken tonight. From 13) _____ dairy section, I usually
buy 14) _____ dozen eggs and 15) _____ milk, but I don't buy 16) _____ cheese.

I get a lot of things from 17) _____ aisle 6: 18) _____ bag of 19) _____ rice,
20) _____ dry beans, and usually 21) _____ package or two of 22) _____ pasta. I try
to move down 23) _____ aisle 5 very quickly so that I won't be tempted by 24) _____
cookies there. I buy 25) _____ bread, of course, but not 26) _____ kind in aisle 5. I
prefer 27) _____ kind of bread they sell in 28) _____ bakery section of 29) _____
store. I don't usually go down 30) _____ beverage* aisle because I don't like 31) _____
soft drinks. But I do go down 32) _____ breakfast-food aisle to get 33) _____ cereal for
34) _____ breakfast.

I love 35) _____ snack foods but try not to buy any because they're pretty expensive and
fattening.* 36) _____ frozen foods also tend to be expensive, but I can't resist ice cream, and
I drink quite a lot of 37) _____ frozen juice.

I like to do my food shopping early in the morning or late at night because there are fewer
shoppers in 38) _____ store then.

*beverage: *a drink*   *fattening: *containing a lot of calories (of food) that make people gain weight*

Articles and Nouns

A/an and the; The 1; The 2 (school / the school, etc.)

Put in *a*/*an* or *the*. Leave the space empty if none of these is possible.

A

When you look up at **1)** _the_ sky, it's usually easy to see **2)** _the_ sun or **3)** _the_ moon, but **4)** _a_ planet like Mars is harder to see in **5)** _–_ space. Of course, if you live near **6)** _____ ocean, there are often **7)** _____ clouds in the sky. And if you live in **8)** _____ country instead of **9)** _____ big city, **10)** _____ stars seem to shine more brightly at night. If **11)** _____ environment is polluted with **12)** _____ smog or light, it's more difficult to look into **13)** _____ space, even on **14)** _____ clear nights. For example, even on **15)** _____ clearest night in Los Angeles, on **16)** _____ West Coast of the United States, it's hard to see as many stars as in **17)** _____ small town in **18)** _____ mountains just 80 miles away. Los Angeles isn't **19)** _____ capital of California, but it's **20)** _____ major U.S. city. It has **21)** _____ same environmental problems as **22)** _____ other large cities in **23)** _____ world.

B

I got out of **1)** _____ bed at 6:00 this morning and had **2)** _____ quick breakfast because I wanted to get to **3)** _____ class early. They had said on **4)** _____ TV and on **5)** _____ radio that traffic would be heavy today because of **6)** _____ big accident near **7)** _____ hospital. They advised people to leave **8)** _____ home early so that they wouldn't get to **9)** _____ work or school late today. So, I made sure I took **10)** _____ earlier bus than usual. I hardly recognized anyone on **11)** _____ bus because it wasn't **12)** _____ one I usually take. But I recognized **13)** _____ lady who goes to **14)** _____ same church as my parents. She teaches writing to **15)** _____ prisoners, and she was on her way to **16)** _____ prison. **17)** _____ roads were full of **18)** _____ cars, but **19)** _____ bus arrived at **20)** _____ college on time.

I've been late to **21)** _____ class three times this month, and **22)** _____ teacher spoke angrily to me about it yesterday. Walking from **23)** _____ bus stop to class, I couldn't help thinking that going to **24)** _____ school is a bit like being in **25)** _____ prison. Five days **26)** _____ week, I go to **27)** _____ same classes and eat my meals at **28)** _____ same times. When I get **29)** _____ home, I start my homework before I eat **30)** _____ dinner, and then my parents turn on **31)** _____ TV while I keep studying. **32)** _____ next morning, it starts all over again. Is **33)** _____ life of a prisoner much different?

The 3 (children / the children); The 4 (the giraffe / the telephone / the piano, etc.; the + Adjective)

Put in _the_ where necessary. If _the_ is not necessary, leave the space empty.

1. ___The___ young are often more honest about their feelings than __–__ adults are.

2. It is a country's responsibility to take care of _____ poor, _____ sick and disabled, and _____ homeless in its population.

3. Are you worried about _____ crime? Do you think _____ poor people are more likely* to become _____ criminals than _____ rich are?

4. Jenny is studying _____ veterinary science because she loves _____ animals a lot.

5. Many people are afraid of _____ snakes, but _____ most snakes are harmless.

6. _____ life in the previous century was harder in many ways than _____ life is today.

7. As a volunteer, Alex isn't paid for _____ work he does with _____ foreign students, but he is paid for teaching _____ writing to _____ deaf students at _____ school for the deaf.

8. Do _____ Swiss still make _____ watches, or are they made mainly by _____ Japanese now?

9. Paul plays _____ football professionally. People are often surprised that he also loves _____ classical music and plays _____ violin very well.

10. A neighbor of mine believes very strongly in taking _____ vitamins and eating _____ local fruits and vegetables rather than imported ones.

11. Sometimes, _____ people with money say _____ unemployed are lazy and don't want to work. _____ most unemployed people I know have simply had _____ bad luck.

12. I know that _____ fish is good for you, but I didn't like _____ fish I had last night. Maybe I should try a different kind of _____ seafood next time.

13. _____ people everywhere in the world need _____ good clean water and _____ nutritious food to be healthy.

14. _____ couples who don't agree about whether to have _____ children probably shouldn't get married to each other.

15. Which invention was more important – _____ car or _____ computer?

16. I like working with _____ students. Working with _____ teachers can be more difficult.

*likely: _probable_

Answer the questions about the items in parentheses. If you're not sure of the answer, begin with *I think*. Include *the* where necessary.

1. Which newspaper has more readers? *(New York Times / Wall Street Journal)*
   (I think) the New York Times has more readers than _the Wall Street Journal._

2. Which is higher? (Empire State Building / Andes Mountains)
   _____ higher than _____

3. Which is busier? (O'Hare Airport in Chicago / Rhine-Main Airport in Frankfurt)
   _____ busier than _____

4. Which country has more people? (Czech Republic / China / Australia)
   _____ than _____

5. Which country has a larger area? (Mexico / Dominican Republic)
   _____

6. Which area has a cooler climate? (north of Europe / Southeast Asia)
   _____

7. Which area has a larger population? (Middle East / Far East)
   _____

8. Which river is longer? (Nile River / Mississippi River)
   _____

9. Which group of islands has a larger population? (Hawaii / Philippines)
   _____

10. Which is longer? (Great Wall of China / Suez Canal)
    _____

11. Which was more difficult to build? (Giza Pyramids / Buckingham Palace)
    _____

12. Which school is more famous? (University of California / Princeton University)
    _____

13. Which body of water is warmer? (North Atlantic / Red Sea)
    _____

14. Who is more famous? (President Kennedy / Queen of Jordan)
    _____

15. Which organization would you rather work for? (International Red Cross / Sony)
    _____

Order the words to make logical sentences. Add *is* or *are* to each sentence. Three are questions.

1. (too small / my jeans / for me) *My jeans are too small for me* .

2. (a long way / ten kilometers / to walk) *Ten kilometers is a long way to walk* .

3. (there / of bird / at the zoo / a new species) _____ .

4. (where / your binoculars) _____ ?

5. (no news / good news) _____ , they say.

6. (a lot of money / fifty dollars / for a book) _____ _____ .

7. (a bicycle / means of transportation / my only) _____ _____ .

8. (new or old / those TV series) _____ _____ ?

9. (all politics / local) A wise man once said that _____ .

10. (a difficult subject / for many students / math) _____ _____ .

11. (there / than firefighters / in this city / more police) _____ _____ .

12. (not / these / my glasses) _____ .

13. (three years / a long time) _____ _____ to spend away from home.

14. (nice people / not necessarily nice) _____ _____ all the time.

15. (a pair of shorts / sometimes more expensive) _____ _____ than a pair of pants.

16. (physics / a difficult subject) _____ .
(electronics and economics / too) _____ .

17. ($35,000 / a big salary) _____ _____ for a new college graduate?

18. (generally good / people) _____ .

Noun + Noun (**a tennis ball / a headache**, etc.)

What do we call these things and people?

1. The bag I use to carry my books is ___*a book bag*___ .

2. Pains that I have in my legs are ___*leg pains*___ .

3. An operation that lasts two hours is ___*a two-hour operation*___ .

4. An athlete who only practices on weekends is _____ .

5. Fish that comes from the ocean is _____ .

6. Problems that I have with money are _____ .

7. A pie made of apples is _____ .

8. Apples that are meant to be cooked in a pie, not eaten fresh, are _____ .

9. Small plates used for salads are _____ .

10. A bill worth 20 dollars is _____ .

11. A chapter that has 40 pages is _____ .

12. A fire station that is 100 years old is _____ .

13. Stamps worth 42 cents are _____ .

14. A day on which workers receive their pay is _____ .

15. A day on which I go to work is _____ .

16. A contract for two years is _____ .

17. A movie that lasts 90 minutes is _____ .

18. A program on the radio that lasts 60 minutes is _____ .

19. A cruise on the ocean for 14 days is _____ .

20. Waves in the ocean that are nine feet high are _____ .

21. Pictures of someone's wedding that are 10 years old are _____

    _____ .

22. A worker in a factory that makes potato chips is _____ .

23. A doctor specializing in hearts who is 29 years old is _____

    _____ .

24. Shoes that cost one hundred dollars and that you wear only to work are _____

    _____ .

-'s (your sister's name) and of . . . (the name of the book)

In some of these sentences, it would be more natural to use -'s or -'. Change the <u>underlined</u> parts where necessary.

1. <u>The owner of my apartment building</u> doesn't live there.   *RIGHT*

2. <u>The children of my brother</u> are very well behaved.   *My brother's children*

3. We didn't see <u>the beginning of the movie</u>.   _____

4. <u>The back of my hand</u> itches.   _____

5. I'm looking forward to <u>the concert of tonight</u>.   _____

6. <u>The bottom of the boat</u> was made of glass.   _____

7. Sally goes to a <u>school of girls</u>.   _____

8. I lost <u>the pay of half a day</u> for being late.   _____

9. I don't want to eat the <u>leftovers* of yesterday</u>.   _____

10. The party's at <u>the house of Glen and Lynn</u>.   _____

11. Tim's office is at <u>the top of the building</u>.   _____

12. Have you met <u>the father of the husband of June</u>?   _____

13. <u>The parks of the city</u> are used a lot.   _____

14. The ball hit me in <u>the side of the face</u>.   _____

15. <u>The population of the world</u> is growing every year.   _____

16. There's room for us in <u>the car of Pam and Phil</u>.   _____

17. What was <u>the name of the restaurant</u> we liked so much?   _____

18. What is <u>the name of the woman</u> who interviewed you?   _____

19. Why do <u>clothes of children</u> cost so much?   _____

20. What time is <u>the baseball game of next week</u>?   _____

21. What is the name of <u>the secretary of Mr. Thompson</u>?   _____

22. What is the name of <u>the brother of the husband of the secretary</u>?   _____

*leftovers: *food remaining from a previous meal*

Articles and Nouns

Read the passage carefully and look for mistakes. The first six mistakes are corrected for you. Find 12 mistakes in the second paragraph and correct them.

Two ~~roommates of college~~ *college roommates* and I hope we can take a trip to ~~the~~ Mexico, Belize, and Guatemala this winter. I have looked into flight *s* to those places, and they're pretty expensive, so I'm working with ~~the~~ *a* travel agent to find the lowest price. So far, the cheapest fares ~~has~~ been over $1,000, so we're still looking for ~~the~~ *a* cheaper one.

We would like to escape from a cold weather at home in Minnesota, visit some pyramid in area, spend some time at the beach, and practice Spanish. Of course, we'll eat new dishes and meet the new people too. My friends think I am only interested in eating, but that opinion is very unfair. To me, the food in new country is an important part of culture of the country. It would be a terrible mistake to go to a foreign country and stay at fancy hotels and eat same food as at home. While in Mexico, we plan to visit the Maya ruins at Chichen Itza. The ruins are located in south of Mexico, near Caribbean Sea. Today, we admire skill of the ancient Maya in architecture, math, and astronomy. They built temples, pyramids, palaces, and observatories* without metal tool. I especially want to see Kukulan, a 2,000-year-old pyramid and temple. The Maya developed advanced civilization when much of the world was still living in primitive conditions.

Follow-up: On a separate piece of paper, write your own paragraph about a trip you would like to take. Tell where, when, and with whom you would like to travel, and why you want to go there. Use articles and nouns carefully.

*observatories: *buildings from which scientists can watch the planets, stars, etc.*

Myself/yourself/themselves, etc.

Put in **-self**, **-selves**, or **each other**. Leave the space empty if the sentence is already complete.

1. I'm sure you'll be able to solve the puzzle if you concentrate __–__ hard.

2. My sister and her fiancé have been mad at ___each other___ since they traveled together.

3. A: Who cut your hair for you?

   B: I cut it ___myself___ .

4. A: What happened to your chin?

   B: Oh, I cut _____ while I was shaving _____ .

5. The volleyball team played well and won. The girls should be proud of

   _____ .

6. A friend of mine and I usually meet _____ at my house before we go to play tennis.

7. I don't think Al and Laurel have known _____ long enough to get married.

8. If parents do everything for their children, the children won't learn to depend on

   _____ .

9. A: Why haven't you told anyone when you're getting married?

   B: Because my fiancé and I aren't sure of the date _____ .

10. After a short time in Canada, Maria could express _____ very well in English.

11. High school reunions give old classmates a chance to see _____ every five or ten years.

12. "Don't shoot _____ in the foot"* is good advice both to a hunter and to someone who acts in anger.

13. My grandparents take good care of _____ by eating right, taking time to relax _____ , and getting enough sleep.

14. "Class, I'll let you introduce _____ to _____ ," Mrs. Smith said to us.

15. Don't blame _____ for what happened. It wasn't your fault.

16. A: How much did it cost to fix your car?

    B: Not too much. We did it _____ .

17. Cindy and Tom really enjoy _____ when they play tennis against

    _____ .

*A common American saying that advises people not to act in a way that is going to end up hurting them.

Pronouns and Determiners

A friend of mine, My own house, By myself

Complete the passages using *my* / *my own* / *me* / *myself, his* / *his own* / *him* / *himself*, etc.

A

My grandfather has lived by 1) _himself_ since my grandmother died a few years ago. We worry about 2) _____ because we think that, at 82, he is too old to live alone.

He has two children, but both of them live hours away, and they both have 3) _____ families to take care of. My father and my aunt have both invited Grandpa to live with 4) _____ and 5) _____ families. But Grandpa prefers living in 6) _____ house. He says he doesn't want to leave the house, friends, and neighbors that he has known for 60 years. Grandpa still drives and gets together with friends of 7) _____ almost every day. We understand that he can still take care of 8) _____ . He shops and cooks, and he pays a teenager from the neighborhood to clean the house every week.

My grandfather says he is doing just fine on 9) _____ . He wants us to visit 10) _____ as often as we can, though. Someone in the family goes to see him almost every week. Sometimes I drive the two hours with a friend of 11) _____ to see how he's doing. As long as he's healthy, I think we need to respect 12) _____ decision to be on 13) _____ .

B

I have been living by 1) _____ for six months now. It's more expensive and a little lonely at times, but I have to say it's not all bad. I've lived on 2) _____ since college, but always with roommates. It's true that I have to do all the cooking 3) _____ now, but I can eat whatever and whenever I want to. I have 4) _____ bedroom now, and I don't have to share 5) _____ bathroom with messy roommates anymore. My old roommates are living by 6) _____ now, too. One of them, Sally, hasn't been able to arrange transportation to work for 7) _____ yet, so I still give 8) _____ a ride in the morning. I think we're all better friends now that we have stopped being roommates.

Follow-up: Do you live on your own or with your family? Are people who live by themselves fortunate or unfortunate? Write on a separate piece of paper to explain your opinion.

There . . . and It . . .

Complete B's answers. Use **there is/was** or **it is/was** + the words in parentheses.

A	**B**

1. Was the storm bad?

(terrible) Yes. _It was terrible._

2. Was the storm bad?

(a lot of damage) Yes. _There was a lot of damage._

3. Why don't we drive to Seattle this weekend?

(too far) No. _____ _____ Let's fly instead.

4. Can I have some cream in my coffee?

(not any cream) Sorry. _____ _____

5. Did you go on a hike last weekend?

(not nice enough) No. _____ _____ It was raining.

6. Can I borrow your camera for the weekend?

(something wrong with it) Sorry. _____ _____

7. Have you heard the news about Rosa?

(wonderful) Yes, I have. _____ _____ that she's getting married.

8. It's a little late, but do you want to stop and see Kevin?

(a light) Why don't we? _____ _____ on in the living room.

9. Amy said to stop by* anytime. Do you want to stop by now?

(too late to stop by) I don't think so. _____ _____ without calling first.

10. Should we serve the rest of the apple pie to our guests for dessert?

(not enough for everyone) We can't. _____ _____

11. Did you like the Argentine film you saw?

(very interesting) Yes, I did. _____ _____

12. Are you going to get a flu shot* this year?

(a lot of flu at work last year) Yes, I think I will. _____ _____

13. What is the weather like in Moscow?

(a lot of snow there last winter) Cold, I think. _____ _____ _____

14. Did you pack everything we need for our trip?

(bound to be) Probably not. _____ _____ something I forgot.

15. Is there still a drugstore at the mall?

(used to be) I'm not sure. _____ _____ one.

*stop by: *to visit for a short time*   *flu shot: *a vaccination against influenza (flu)*

Pronouns and Determiners

Some and any

Complete the passages with **some, any, somebody / -thing / -where,** or **anybody / -thing / -where.**

A

1) _Something_ strange happened the other day at the supermarket. I was buying

2) _some_ groceries when 3) _____ started talking to me. He asked, "How's it going, Mike?" My name isn't Mike, and I didn't recognize the man, so I was confused. I tried to place his face, but I couldn't think of 4) _____ I might have met him. He just went on talking, and I kept trying to think of 5) _____ to say. Finally, I told him that I was not his friend Mike and that I didn't even know

6) _____ called Mike. Now *he* was confused. Obviously, I looked like

7) _____ that he knew. Finally, he said, "I'm sorry. I didn't mean to cause

8) _____ trouble. You look just like 9) _____ that I used to work with at Acme Computers."

The strange part of all this is that I have worked at Acme Computers for five years! But I knew I didn't know the man *or* "Mike." "That's all right," I said. "10) _____ can make a mistake." I thought it would be better not to say 11) _____ about working at Acme, though. Strange world!

B

My neighbors are looking for their lost parakeet.* They saw it fly out the door, so they know it's not 1) _____ in the house. They're worried it won't find

2) _____ to eat or drink outside, or that a cat or other animal will catch it. If 3) _____ finds it, they'll get a reward of $25. Pretty Boy is blue and may still be 4) _____ in the neighborhood. Personally, I don't think they have

5) _____ chance of seeing the bird again. Hardly 6) _____ finds a lost parakeet. In a mild climate like ours, a parakeet can survive on its own, I'm sure. And I don't think 7) _____ parakeet would give up a life in the wild* to live in a cage again.

*parakeet: *a small colorful tropical bird*   *in the wild: *in nature, not in a zoo or a home*

No/none/any, Nothing/nobody, etc.

Answer the questions two ways: (a) with a short answer using *none*, *no one*, *nothing*, or *nowhere*; and (b) with a full sentence using not + *any*, *anyone*, *anything*, or *anywhere*.

1. How many eggs did you break?
   _____None_____ . I _____didn't break any eggs_____ .

2. What are you doing tonight?
   _____Nothing_____ . I _____ .

3. Who did you tell about my speeding ticket?*
   _____ . I _____ .

4. Where are the Smiths going on vacation this year?
   _____ . They _____ .

5. How much money do I owe you?
   _____ . You _____ .

6. What did Fred say about me?
   _____ . He _____ .

7. Where do you want to go tomorrow?
   _____ . I _____ .

8. How much free time does Rob have?
   _____ . He _____ .

9. Who did you give money to?
   _____ . I _____ .

10. Where did you put my wallet?
    _____ . I _____ .

11. Who did you talk to about my party?
    _____ . We _____ .

12. What's wrong with your car?
    _____ . There _____ .

13. How many speeding tickets have you gotten?
    _____ . I _____ .

14. What were you going to say?
    _____ . I _____ .

*speeding ticket: *a note saying you have to pay money for driving too fast*

UNIT
84

Read what an angry mother is telling her 16-year-old son about his responsibilities at home. Then complete the passage with *no*, *any*, *none*, *nothing*, or *nobody*.

Mother: Don't tell me you have 1) __*no*__ time to help out at home. I don't care if

2) _____ of your friends have to do chores* around the house. Maybe

your friends don't have parents who both work. But that doesn't make

3) _____ difference. 4) _____ child should grow

up without helping the family. We give you an allowance* to teach you to handle*

money. You can spend it in 5) _____ way that you want. We give

you chores to do to teach you responsibility. 6) _____ of the chores is

very hard or takes much time. There will be 7) _____ excuses for not

doing your chores. Is that absolutely clear?

Son: But Mom, you and Dad always say that 8) _____ is more important

than my education. If 9) _____ helps me with these dishes, I won't

have 10) _____ time to do my homework. Besides,

11) _____ of my friends has to wash dishes. I feel like

12) _____ understands me.

Mother: I understand you better than you think. I am not raising 13) _____ lazy,

irresponsible children. To make sure you have enough time for homework, there will

be absolutely 14) _____ TV or computer games for you for the next

few days. Maybe then you can manage to do your chores and your homework.

Son: Yes, Mom.

chore: a household job that has to be done regularly, such as washing dishes or taking garbage outside
*allowance: money that parents give children regularly   *handle: to deal with, manage, control*

Much, many, little, few, a lot, plenty

Find the mistakes and correct them. If there are no mistakes, write RIGHT.

1. Diane comes from a small family. She has very ~~little~~ ^{few} relatives. _____

2. I don't know many people who live alone. _RIGHT_

3. My brother spends much time fixing his car. _____

4. We won't have trouble finding a place to stay in Los Angeles. There are plenty hotels there. _____

5. Martha is a lucky woman. She has a few enemies. _____

6. I have very little money on me, so I can't treat you to lunch today. Sorry. _____

7. Josh has lots clothes. Why does he need to borrow yours? _____

8. My grandparents are very active. They go out much. _____

9. Mr. James isn't a very good boss. He has a little patience. _____

10. It cost very little to fix my car. Was I lucky! _____

11. There aren't much reasons to visit that town unless you like old mines. _____

12. I ate few hours ago, but I'm hungry again. _____

13. I haven't gone to the beach on vacation for a lot of years. _____

14. Jason knows a lot of people, but he doesn't have lots of close friends. _____

15. We're lucky. We've gotten plenty help from friends with our new baby. _____

16. "Do you know anything about computers?" "Little. What do you need?" _____

17. There were only few students who didn't bring their books to class. _____

18. I'm busy at work. A lot of days, I don't have time to eat lunch. _____

19. How have you been? I haven't seen you for a few months. _____

20. Do you go to the movies much? _____

21. I've spent a little time in the Netherlands, but I can't speak much Dutch. _____

22. She's gone to Rio a few time, but she doesn't know the city very well. _____

Pronouns and Determiners

All / all of, most / most of, no / none of, etc.
Both / both of, neither / neither of, either / either of

Complete the sentences using the words in parentheses. Sometimes you need to add _the_, _of_, or _of the_.

1. (most / people) We invited ___most of the people___ that we know to our daughter's wedding.

2. (neither / answer) Ben solved the math problem two different ways, but ___neither answer___ was right.

3. Jake's grandfather is not very well. (most / days) He spends _____ in bed.

4. (both / presents) Julia couldn't decide whether to get her sister a bracelet or a camera, so she got _____ .

5. (both / them) Ken and Sarah wanted to go to the concert with us, but there weren't enough tickets for _____ .

6. (either / his brothers) Joe doesn't talk to _____ very often.

7. (either / author) Mark recommended two books to me, but I had never heard of _____ .

8. We went to Los Angeles for the weekend. (both / days) We spent _____ with friends who live there.

9. (some / days) _____ the weather here is beautiful, but other days it's very gray.

10. (neither / presents) _____ cost a lot, but Jeremy was very pleased with both of them.

11. (some / cars) _____ are safer than others.

12. (some / money) I think Brenda spent _____ that I lent her on a new sweater instead of food!

13. We couldn't decide where to eat. (half / our group) _____ wanted to eat Mexican food, and the others wanted Japanese food.

14. Both Claudia and her sister want to visit Australia next summer. (neither / them) _____ has been there before.

15. Does your friend ever go home? (all / time) It seems like he's here _____ .

16. (half / this medicine) I have to take _____ now and the rest tomorrow morning.

All / all of, most / most of, no / none of, etc.
Both / both of, neither / neither of, either / either of

Complete the descriptions of the picture. Use **all (of)**, **none (of)**, **both (of)**, **neither (of)**, or **either (of)**.

U N I T S
86–87

1.   __*All*__ the basketball players are wearing uniforms.

2.   __*None of*__ them are playing basketball in street clothes.

3.   _____ the girls has short hair.

4.   _____ the boys have short hair.

5.   _____ the girls is taller than the boys.

6.   The girl with the ball doesn't want _____ the boys to get it.

7.   _____ the players is an adult. They are _____ teenagers.

8.   _____ team has five players.

9.   _____ the girls is wearing a sweatband, but _____ the boys are.

10. _____ these teenagers are wearing athletic shoes.

11. _____ teams are playing well. _____ team could win.

12. _____ team looks tired. _____ teams seem full of energy.

13. _____ the players are sitting down and relaxing.

14. It seems that _____ the players are having fun.

Complete the passage. Use *all*, *each*, *every*, *everyone*, or *whole*.

My friend Rob is a good friend, but he can be inflexible* sometimes. I mean, he has to have things his own way* or he's not happy. For example, Rob takes a two-week vacation from the bank 1) __*every*__ August. His wife and children always want to go away somewhere, but Rob insists on spending 2) __*all*__ his vacations working in the yard at home. Last year he spent the 3) _____ two weeks of vacation working in his vegetable garden. 4) _____ else in the family wanted to go to Vancouver, but Rob would not go. Since he did not want to go, the 5) _____ family had to miss a nice vacation.

6) _____ four or five weeks, Rob, some other friends, and I meet to play golf, have dinner, or do something else together. When a lot of people go out to dinner together, it's usually easier to split the bill:* 7) _____ person pays an equal share. But Rob never agrees to split the bill – he insists on paying for exactly what he ordered, no more and no less. This can be embarrassing for 8) _____ else in the group. We have to sit there waiting while Rob takes out his calculator to figure out *his* bill.

9) _____ of us were really upset with Rob the last time this happened because the waiter became very impatient with us. We should have asked for separate checks.* Some of our friends have made fun of* Rob's inflexibility when the bill comes, but he doesn't see what the problem is. He thinks his behavior is normal and fair to 10) _____ .

It might seem that 11) _____ Rob thinks about is himself, but in truth, he is a very nice person. He is ready to help 12) _____ – and anyone. He respects and treats 13) _____ person the same, no matter who they are. Of our 14) _____ group of friends, he's the only one who remembers 15) _____'s birthday. And he knows 16) _____ child's name in 17) _____ our families. I guess we just have to accept him the way he is. That's 18) _____ we can do.

Follow-up: In your opinion, should everyone behave the same way? Think of at least one person in your own group of friends who behaves differently, and write about him or her on a separate piece of paper. Explain your opinion of what is the best way to handle people who behave differently from you.

---

*inflexible: *unwilling to change your way of doing things*   *have things (your) own way: *to have what you want*
*split the bill: *to divide the cost and share equally*   * separate checks: *separate bills for each person's order in a restaurant*
*make fun of (someone): *to make a joke about (someone) in a way that is not kind*

Pronouns and Determiners

Use your own ideas to complete the sentences about yourself.

1. I have a lot of _free time_ , but I don't have much _money_ .
   I have a lot of _work to do_ , but I don't have much _desire to do it_ .
   I have a lot of _____ , but I don't have much _____ .

2. I was invited to two parties. Both were _____ .
   Neither of them _____ .

3. I like most _____ , but
   I don't have many _____ .

4. I have very few problems with _____ . I have
   a little trouble with _____ , though.

5. Most of my friends are _____ , and about half of
   them _____ .

6. Most people don't _____ themselves.

7. My parents are both _____ . They
   _____ each other.

8. No one in my family _____ , but all of us
   _____ .

9. None of my friends _____ , but a few of them
   _____ .

10. Some of my _____ have decided to _____
    _____ .

11. Almost all of the _____ are _____ .
    Not many of them _____ .

12. Some people _____ their own _____ , but not many do.

13. There are _____ in my town, and most of them
    _____ .

14. Few people understand _____ .

15. Anyone can _____ , but no one can
    _____ .

Relative Clauses

Relative Clauses 1: Clauses with **who/that/which**

Are these sentences right or wrong? Correct them where necessary.

1. San Francisco is a pretty city which is
   known for its views and hilly streets.   _RIGHT_____

2. I need a friend who he is ready to help
   when I need help.   _who is ready to help_____

3. Are we going to see the movie it were
   advertised on TV?   _that was advertised on TV_____

4. Did you go to the wedding that was held
   outside on the beach?   _____

5. Roger bought a thank-you card for a teacher
   which helped him a lot during the year.   _____

6. Roger also bought presents for two
   classmates what is moving away.   _____

7. I don't see the man he told us to meet
   him here.   _____

8. What did you do with the money that was
   on the table?   _____

9. We wrote to the Mexican man which was
   so hospitable to us in Oaxaca.   _____

10. Many teenagers like music who have a
    social message or that say something about
    their lives.   _____

11. David forgot to tell me the name of the
    store what sells photo equipment.   _____

12. What happened to the family that used to
    live next door to you?   _____

13. Did you hear from the old friend who
    promised to write?   _____

14. Lynne is only applying to colleges that has
    good programs in music.   _____

15. I've given an invitation to everyone that
    is here.   _____

Relative Clauses 2: Clauses with and without **who/that/which**

Some of these sentences need *who* or *that*. Some have an unnecessary pronoun (*they*, *it*, *them*, etc.). Correct the sentences where necessary.

1. The book I learn grammar from is very good.

   RIGHT

2. What did you do with the letters they were on the table?

   What did you do with the letters that were on the table?

3. Are you going to buy the book you're looking at it?

   Are you going to buy the book you're looking at?

4. We liked the places Rob recommended.

5. Where is the restaurant you ate at it with friends the other night?

6. Mike applied for a job was advertised on the Internet.

7. The hotel we stayed at was really nice.

8. Good friends are the ones you can rely on them.

9. Don't blame me for something someone else did it.

10. The car Mike has had so much trouble with broke down again.

11. Do you agree with the suggestion Sue made at the meeting?

12. I wonder if you found a pair of glasses I might have left them in your café yesterday afternoon.

13. How can I trust someone he lies to me?

14. This store never has anything it fits me.

15. Phoebe was accepted by the college she was hoping to get into it.

16. Do you still write to the people you went to Asia with?

Relative Clauses

Relative Clauses 2: Clauses with and without **who/that/which**; Relative Clauses 3: **whose/whom/where**

Which completions are correct for each sentence? Circle one or two choices.

1. Is this the box _____ you were looking for?   a. who   (b. that)   c. what   (d. –)

2. Did you return the call of the man _____ phoned three times?   a. he   (b. who)   c. which   d. –

3. Do you know the woman _____ husband just died?   (a. whose)   b. her   c. who her   d. –

4. I'll never forget the first time _____ I drove a car.   a. when   b. that   c. which   d. –

5. Do you know the name of the song _____ we just listened to?   a. what   b. that   c. who   d. –

6. Sylvia hasn't seen the people _____ she used to work with.   a. who   b. which   c. with whom   d. –

7. Have you eaten all the fruit _____ was in the bowl on the table?   a. who   b. which   c. it   d. –

8. Please just do _____ I told you to do.   a. that   b. which   c. what   d. –

9. Mary Lou said something _____ I didn't like.   a. that   b. what   c. to which   d. –

10. Mary Lou said something _____ was both unkind and untrue.   a. that   b. it   c. which   d. –

11. They are moving to a place _____ the weather is warmer.   a. where   b. that   c. whose   d. –

12. Have you seen the movie _____ everyone is talking about?   a. that   b. what   c. whom   d. –

13. We congratulated the people _____ son won a scholarship.   a. their   b. whose   c. who their   d. –

14. The restaurant _____ I like to eat closed last month.   a. that   b. where   c. which   d. –

15. The people _____ you live with are very nice.   a. whose   b. that   c. with whom   d. –

16. I've done everything _____ I was supposed to do.   a. what   b. that   c. who   d. –

17. You can eat _____ you want. I don't care.   a. that   b. which   c. what   d. –

18. I forget the reason _____ Sam changed jobs.   a. why   b. who   c. which   d. –

Complete the sentences using relative clauses with **who, whose, whom, where, that**, or **why**.
Form the relative clauses from what the people say.

My father is very rich.

1. My brother is engaged to a woman
   whose father is very rich .

I'm afraid of heights.

2. I know a firefighter _who is afraid of_
   heights .

We stayed there on our honeymoon.

3. The couple showed us pictures of the
   hotel _where they stayed on their_
   honeymoon .

I have fallen in love with her.

4. The woman with _whom he has fallen_
   in love is older than he is.

My wife wants a bigger house.

5. His wife has never told him the reason
   _____
   _____ .

We got married today.

6. I met a nice young couple on the day
   _____
   _____ .

EXERCISE CONTINUES ▶▶

UNIT
92

I want to be a soccer player when I grow up.

7. I enjoyed talking to the girl _____

_____

_____ .

My wife and my daughter both work as police officers in this station.

8. The man pointed to the police station ____

_____

_____ .

I am moving to a new apartment.

Sheila

9. I forget the reason _____ Sheila

_____

_____ .

People get passports here.

10. The two women went downtown to the

building _____

_____ .

I sold my car to her.

11. The woman to _____

_____

_____ keeps calling him with questions.

Our anniversary was last week.

12. I sent a card to my friends _____

_____ .

Relative Clauses 4 & 5: Extra Information Clauses 1 & 2

Make one sentence from two. Use *which*, *whose*, *many of whom*, or *most of whom*.

dolphin

ostrich

donkey

eagle

elephant

tusk

hunters

kangaroo

llama

camel

rattlesnake

shark

goat

1. Dolphins often jump above the surface of the water. (They are actually mammals* rather than fish.)

    Dolphins, *which are actually mammals rather than fish, often jump above the surface of the water* .

2. Ostriches can run very fast. (This is important because they can't fly.)

    Ostriches *can run very fast, which is important because they can't fly* .

3. Dolphins can communicate different kinds of information by making sounds. (Their brains are slightly larger than human brains.)

    Dolphins _____

    _____ .

EXERCISE CONTINUES ▶▶

*mammal: *animal that gives birth to live babies rather than laying eggs*

4. Americans sometimes compare a foolish or stubborn* person to a donkey. (It is an animal in the horse family with short legs and long ears.)

Americans _____

_____ .

5. Eagles eat small animals. (Their sharp beaks and very good sight help them hunt.)

Eagles _____

_____ .

6. Elephants are protected in many countries. (This saves them from being killed for their tusks.)

Elephants _____

_____ .

7. Elephants are still being killed by hunters. (Many of them hunt illegally.)

Elephants _____

_____ .

8. The kangaroo carries its young in its pouch. (A pouch is like a big pocket made of skin.)

The kangaroo _____

_____ .

9. The llama is at home in the Andes Mountains of South America. (Its wool is soft and expensive.)

The llama _____

_____ .

10. I have always been fascinated* by camels. (They are known to travel long distances without water.)

I _____

_____ .

11. Many people are afraid of rattlesnakes and sharks. (Most of them have never seen these animals in the wild.*)

Many people _____

_____ .

12. Goats live wild in mountain areas or are kept on farms. (Their reputation* for eating anything is well known.)

Goats _____

_____ .

*stubborn: *opposed to changing your opinion*   *fascinated (by): *interested (in)*   *in the wild: *in nature, not in a zoo or a home*   *reputation: *the opinion that people in general have about someone/something*

Complete the sentences using the correct form of the verbs in the boxes.

~~build~~	enter	hold	~~host*~~

1. The country _hosting_ the summer Olympics for the first time in 2008 was China. The main site _built_ for the 2008 Olympics is called the National Stadium, also known as the Bird's Nest. People around the world enjoyed watching the opening ceremonies* _____ inside the Bird's Nest on August 8, 2008. In those ceremonies, we were able to see all the national teams _____ the stadium.

call	dominate*	win

2. Park Tae Hwan received South Korea's first Olympic gold medal _____ by a swimmer. Koreans are especially proud of winning an event _____ by Westerners for so many years. At the time he won, Park was an 18-year-old swimmer _____ "Marine Boy" by many Koreans.

fight	wait	win

3. The two players _____ for the ball in this photo are from Australia and Belarus. There are two teammates _____ to see the results of the struggle.* The team _____ the game were the Australians. The score was 83 to 63.

consider	run

4. The athlete _____ in the picture is Usain Bolt, who set three world records in the 2008 Olympics. As in all Olympics, some athletes _____ the best in the world didn't qualify for the finals.

*host: *to provide the place and other necessary things for a special event*   *ceremonies: *special acts performed on important occasions*   *dominate: *to be the most important person or thing*   *struggle: *a fight or difficulty*

Relative Clauses

Use your own ideas to complete these sentences.

1. I would like to talk to someone who _has been to the United Arab Emirates_ .
   I would like to talk to someone who _will be completely honest with me_ .
   I would like to talk to someone who _____ .

2. I would like to have met _Mahatma Gandhi_ , who _used peaceful protest to change_
   his country .
   I would like to have met _____ , who _____
   _____ .

3. I like most people, but I have trouble with people who _____
   _____ .

4. Recently I bought something which _____ .

5. A friend of mine _____ , which upset
   her family a lot.

6. Two things I can't live without are _____
   _____ .

7. I've always dreamed of going to _____ , where _____
   _____ .

8. _____ is a country where you can _____ .

9. English is a language spoken _____ .

10. Recently I saw a woman wearing _____
    _____ .

11. The other day I met a man whose _____
    _____ .

12. The other day I met _____ , whose _____
    _____ .

13. I'll always remember the day that _____ .

14. My family will never understand the reason that I _____
    _____ .

15. The people my friends are married to _____ .

16. The place I go to when I need peace and quiet is _____ .

17. The reason I'm interested in English is that _____ .

Adjectives Ending in -ing and -ed (boring/bored, etc.)

Complete B's answers. Use is, are, was, were, or will be + an -ing or -ed adjective made from the verb in parentheses.

A	**B**

1. How did you like the film?

   (interest) It _was interesting_ .

2. Why doesn't the cat want to go outside?

   (frighten) It _'s frightened_ .

3. What does your brother think of the political scandal?

   (disgust) He _____ . He expects more of politicians.

4. How was your doctor's appointment?

   (depress) It _____ . The doctor said my health was very poor.

5. What did you think of the movie?

   (upset) It _____ because of all the violence.

6. Is Monica going to the movies with us tonight?

   (interest) No, I don't think she _____ _____ in going.

7. Did you enjoy your vacation?

   (disappoint) No, we _____ very _____ . The weather was terrible.

8. Do you understand the directions on this bottle?

   (confuse) No, I don't. I think they _____ _____ .

9. When are your parents leaving for China?

   (excite) Next week. They _____ _____ about going.

10. Did you like the play last night?

    (amuse) Yes, it _____ .

11. How was your job interview?

    (embarrass) I _____ because I answered the questions badly.

12. How will the weather be while we are in Quebec?

    (freeze) I think it _____ . Make sure you pack warm clothes.

13. Were there a lot of people at the party?

    (surprise) Yes, there _____ a _____ number of people there.

14. Should we continue driving or stop for the night?

    (exhaust) If we drive through the night, we _____ tomorrow.

15. Can you believe how childishly Stan behaves sometimes?

    (shock) No, I can't. I think his behavior _____ .

16. Do you really think I'd enjoy the new comedy on TV?

    (bore) Yes, watch it. You _____ _____ , I promise.

Complete the sentences. Use the adjectives in parentheses plus _and_ if necessary.

1. (ill / elderly* / Ukrainian)
    Jared is visiting his seriously _ill elderly Ukrainian_ aunt in the hospital this afternoon.

2. (green / large / woolen)
    I'm looking for a _____ sweater for my father for his birthday.

3. (old / big / beautiful / stone)
    Gary and Paula bought a _____ house.

4. (16-year-old / typical / city)
    My nephew is a _____ boy.

5. (blue / German / big / old)
    My uncle drives a _____ car.

6. (cute / brown / Persian / gray)
    I've lost my _____ kitten.

7. (Argentine / favorite / traditional)
    Gloria's parents like to listen to their _____ music.

8. (new / Thai / great)
    Let's go to that _____ restaurant tonight.

9. (blue / yellow / red)
    I don't think you should wear your brown pants with that _____ shirt.

10. (old / beautiful / Central Asian)
    Susan spent all her money on _____ jewelry.

11. (nice / foreign / young)
    My brother has a lot of _____ friends.

12. (metal / imported / modern)
    The young couple bought _____ furniture for their new home.

13. (Italian / aged / delicious)
    Do you have any of that _____ cheese today?

14. (nice / small / old)
    We stayed at a(n) _____ hotel by the seaside.

15. (good-looking / blond / tall)
    The Judkins raised four _____ children.

*elderly: _old_

Adjectives and Adverbs 1 (quick/quickly)

Complete the second sentence, keeping the same meaning.

1. Cindy's paintings are beautiful.
    Cindy paints __beautifully__ .

2. Don doesn't drive very safely.
    Don isn't a __very safe__ driver.

3. Mark is an incredibly quick typist.
    Mark types _____ .

4. Marcia speaks French really fluently.
    Marcia is _____ in French.

5. Julia is a slow but careful worker.
    Julia works _____ .

6. Paul is talking very strangely for some reason.
    Paul's voice sounds _____ .

7. Mrs. Grey gave the dress a careful and close look before buying it.
    Mrs. Grey looked at _____ .

8. We have had heavy and continuous rain for three days.
    It has rained _____ .

9. Jim was injured in the accident, but the injury wasn't serious.
    Jim wasn't _____ .

10. It was surprising how quick Pat's recovery from her illness was.
    Pat recovered _____ .

11. My boss answered my question coldly and incompletely.
    My boss's answer to my question seemed _____ .

12. The seriousness of this situation is extreme, I think.
    This _____ seems _____ to me.

13. It is incredible how energetic and active my grandmother is.
    My grandmother leads an _____ life.

14. The writer of this composition was hasty* and careless.
    This composition was _____ written.

*hasty: *in a hurry*

Adjectives and Adverbs 2 (well/fast/late, hard/hardly)

A. Complete the passage with *fast*, *hard*, *hardly*, *late*, *lately*, *good*, or *well*.

Things have changed around the office where I work. We are all trying very 1) _hard_ to
please the boss, Mr. Brown. He has been in a bad mood 2) _lately_ , and of course we want
to stay on his good side.* Maybe he doesn't feel 3) _well_ , or maybe something happened
that we don't know about. Anyway, nobody in the office gets to work 4) _late_ anymore.
We stay at work 5) _____ if necessary, we work 6) _____ , and
we treat the customers 7) _____ . Now we take only half an hour for lunch,
so we have to eat very 8) _____ . We 9) _____ have time to
eat a sandwich. I am not sure what is bothering Mr. Brown, but I hope he gets over* it
10) _____ . All the workers like him because he has always treated us
11) _____ . He 12) _____ ever gets angry. We work a long day,
but we are paid 13) _____ . We all hope that Mr. Brown returns to his normal
14) _____ mood soon.

B. Are the underlined words right or wrong? Correct the wrong ones.

1. I am paid <u>well</u>, but I also work very
   <u>hardly</u>.

   RIGHT; hard _____

2. The singer is <u>well known</u> here, but he's
   <u>hardly</u> known at all in other countries.

   _____

3. I'm quite sure you'll remember that
   man's name if you <u>hardly think</u>.

   _____

4. I could <u>hardly</u> believe my eyes when Josh
   walked into work two hours <u>lately</u>.

   _____

5. Margaret is always <u>well dressed</u> even
   though she isn't paid very <u>good</u>.

   _____

6. It's better to arrive <u>lately</u> than never.

   _____

7. I <u>hardly</u> think it matters if some people
   are <u>well paid</u> and others aren't.

   _____

8. If you try <u>hardly</u>, success will come <u>fast</u>.

   _____

9. Sam is very <u>good-looking</u> but not very
   <u>well educated</u>.

   _____

10. I haven't been sleeping <u>good late</u>. I used
    to sleep better.

   _____

*stay on someone's good side: *not to do anything to annoy the person*   *get over (something): *to return to your
normal state (of health, happiness, etc.)*

So and such

Complete the sentences. Use the words in parentheses with *so* or *such*. Use an appropriate tense.

1. Sam _____was in such a hurry_____ (be / in a hurry) this morning that he forgot his keys.

2. Sam _____was so nervous_____ (be / nervous) this morning that he forgot his keys.

3. We _____ (have / much food at home) that I don't think we should go out to eat.

4. Ann _____ (have / a bad cold) recently that she is going to stay home from work tomorrow.

5. It _____ (be / cold) that I didn't walk to work this morning.

6. We didn't say good-bye to Kevin at the party last night because he _____ _____ (look / busy).

7. Let's not take the back road. It _____ (be / old) that it will take longer to get to the city that way.

8. We didn't want to leave the party because we _____ _____ (have / a good time).

9. Why don't we go to the movies tonight? We _____ _____ (not go / for a long time).

10. My essay _____ (have / many mistakes) that I had to do it over.

11. If my grandparents _____ (not live / far away), I would visit them more often.

12. The Holdens spend a lot on repairs because they _____ _____ (live / in an old house).

13. Sarah _____ (spend / much time) traveling to work by train that she always takes a book to read.

14. I'm surprised. I didn't expect the weather _____ (be / nice) today.

15. The Greens _____ (have / a nice time) on vacation in Hawaii that they thought of moving there.

16. I would visit my grandparents more often if it _____ (not / take / long) to drive there.

A. Put the words in parentheses in the correct order to make sentences. Four are questions.

1. (too / speech / follow / to / was / easily / disorganized / his)
   His speech was too disorganized to follow easily.

2. (isn't / enough / Mrs. Garcia / to live by herself / healthy)
   _____

3. (to wear / was / for Millie / jacket / too / the / small)
   _____

4. (enough / isn't / car / Josh / drive / a / to / old)
   _____

5. (nice / such a terrible thing / do / is / George / too / to)
   _____

6. (enough / you / do / to lend me some / have / money / ?)
   _____

7. (on time / enough / this / fast / type / report / I / to finish / can't)
   _____

8. (water on Mars / is / enough / life / to support / there / ?)
   _____

9. (this letter / enough / know / German / you / do / to translate / ?)
   _____

10. (too / shirt / is / this / big / me / for / ?)
    _____

11. (chairs / there / for / aren't / to sit down / enough / everyone)
    _____

B. Rewrite sentences 2 – 5. Use *too* instead of *enough*, or *enough* instead of *too*. Substitute the words in parentheses, and make any other necessary changes.

1. (organized) _His speech was not organized enough to follow easily._

2. (sick) _____ too sick _____

3. (big) _____

4. (young) _____

5. (mean) _____

Adjectives and Adverbs

EXERCISE

128

Review of **-ing** and **-ed** adjectives; word order; **-ly** ending;
well/fast/late/hard/hardly; **so/such**; **enough/too**

UNITS
96–101

Circle the best completion(s).

1. I walked out of the movie because it was _____ .
   a. so boring   b. such boring   c. being boring

2. You look _____ . Why don't you take a _____ nap?*
   a. exhausting / quick   b. exhausting / quickly   c. exhausted / quick

3. How can I study when I feel _____ ?
   a. very tiring   b. so tired   c. too tiredly

4. We bought a _____ car.
   a. black German beautiful   b. beautiful black German   c. German black beautiful

5. I got to work _____ , so I _____ had time to prepare for my meeting.
   a. lately / hard   b. late / hard   c. late / hardly

6. Walking in the rain is _____ when you live in the desert.
   a. such pleasant   b. such a pleasure   c. so pleased

7. I have _____ , but I'm _____ to travel abroad this year.
   a. enough money / too busy   b. too much money / free enough
   c. enough time / too rich

8. I'm not _____ to stay home today.
   a. so sick   b. too sick   c. sick enough

9. The movie was _____ and not _____ .
   a. such a long / interested   b. too long / interesting enough   c. so long / too interested

10. We have a _____ engineer at our company.
    a. brilliant new French   b. new French brilliant   c. French brilliant new

11. They work _____ and eat _____ .
    a. hardly / quickly   b. hard / quick   c. hard / fast

12. We waited _____ that in the end we felt _____ .
    a. so long / frustrated   b. such a long time / frustrating   c. so long / frustrating

13. I know Ted pretty _____ , but I _____ know his wife.
    a. good / hardly   b. well / hardly   c. well / hard

14. Joan finished her work _____ .
    a. amazingly quick   b. amazing quickly   c. amazingly quickly

15. Bob's mother cooked _____ food for us.
    a. authentic* Thai delicious   b. Thai delicious authentic   c. delicious authentic Thai

16. Are you _____ with how _____ you are in English?
    a. satisfying / fluently   b. satisfying / fluent   c. satisfied / fluent

*take a nap: *to sleep for a short time, usually during the day*   *authentic: *real, true*

135

Adjectives and Adverbs

Comparison 1 (cheaper, more expensive, etc.)

Complete the sentences using the comparative form (*older* / *more important*, etc.).

1. You're driving too fast. Could you please drive *more slowly* ?

2. Kim is too nervous to talk now. Wait till she's a little *calmer* .

3. This house is too old-fashioned. I'd like to live in a house that's _____ .

4. These shirts are pretty expensive. Don't you have any that are _____ ?

5. Glen's sick today. Let's not visit him until he's feeling _____ .

6. I'm a little heavy now. I'll be able to wear these pants when I'm _____ .

7. This book is too hard for me. Do you have one that is _____ to understand?

8. We had driven 500 miles but decided to drive a little _____ before stopping.

9. We stayed up too late last night. Tonight we're going to bed _____ .

10. This rental car* is too small for five people. Let's get one that's _____ .

11. We can't hear you in the back of the room. Could you please speak _____ ?

12. Our teacher is too easy on us. I'd like a teacher who is _____ .

13. This road looks a little dangerous to me. Can't we take one that's _____ ?

14. My mechanic is too careless. I'm going to find one who works _____ .

15. My doctor's good, but he's pretty unfriendly. I'd like a doctor who's _____ .

16. My headache is bad, but I won't go to the doctor unless it gets _____ .

17. I find watching TV boring. Can't we do something _____ ?

18. Sorry to interrupt you. I just have one question, and there will be no _____ interruptions.

19. Ken is a good friend, but Mike has been a _____ one.

20. These flowers are very pretty. I don't think you'll find any that are _____ .

21. The roads are crowded, but if we wait until rush hour to leave, they will just get _____ .

22. I was hoping the team would do better this year, but they've actually done _____ .

23. My roommate always makes a lot of noise when he comes home. I wish he would come in _____ .

24. I don't know Joe very well, but I'd like to know him _____ .

*rental car: *a car rented from a company for a day, a week, etc.*

Comparison 2 (much better / any better / better and better / the sooner the better); Comparison 3 (as . . . as / than)

Choose the best completion for each sentence.

1. "Does Max miss work a lot?"   "Not really. In fact, he doesn't miss work nearly __c__ as you do."
   a. as frequent   b. more frequent   c. as often

2. Karen's too nervous to talk now. Wait till she's _____ calmer.
   a. a bit   b. more   c. the more

3. I don't know many people who are _____ as Sarah.
   a. nicer   b. as much nice   c. as nice

4. The longer I know Sam, the _____ I understand him.
   a. well   b. little   c. less

5. I'm looking for a mechanic who's a little _____ than the one I have now.
   a. as careful   b. more carefully   c. more careful

6. "Have you gotten _____ at tennis?"   "No, I play about the same."
   a. less badly   b. less worse   c. any better

7. Gloria eats _____ than anyone I know, but she stays thin.
   a. as much   b. as many   c. more

8. _____ you talk to me, the sooner I'll finish this work.
   a. As little as   b. The less   c. The little

9. Mr. Roth isn't as impatient _____ the other teachers in this school.
   a. more   b. than   c. as

10. I should have gotten the job. I'm much _____ than the other applicants were.
    a. more experienced   b. as experienced   c. less experienced

11. I love spring. The days are getting _____ .
    a. more and more warm   b. any warmer   c. warmer and warmer

12. "Are you and Kim the same age?"   "Actually, I'm _____ ."
    a. slightly older   b. as older   c. nearly younger

13. _____ money you have, the more you seem to spend.
    a. The little   b. As little   c. The less

14. Sam got the job because the other applicants weren't as well qualified _____ .
    a. than him   b. than he was   c. as he was

15. _____ we leave, the easier the drive will be.
    a. As soon as   b. The sooner   c. As early as possible

Adjectives and Adverbs

Comparison 1, 2, 3

UNITS
102–104

Complete the second sentence, keeping the same meaning.

1. I'm taller than you are.
   You aren't *as tall as I am* .

2. They didn't have as much fun as we did.
   We had *more fun than they did* .

3. I don't have as much free time as you do.
   You have _____ I do.

4. Paul looks worse today than he did yesterday.
   He doesn't _____ he did yesterday.

5. Jack talks less than his brother.
   Jack doesn't _____ his brother.

6. I don't drive as far to work as Kate does.
   Kate drives _____ I do.

7. Sarah isn't as friendly as she used to be.
   Sarah used _____ she is now.

8. Martin answered the question less intelligently than I expected.
   Martin didn't _____ .

9. There were fewer people at the game than usual.
   There weren't _____ .

10. These shoes aren't as uncomfortable as they look.
    These shoes are _____ .

11. I did worse on the test than I'd hoped.
    I didn't _____ .

12. Gas costs double what it did a few years ago.
    Gas costs twice _____ .

13. Ana doesn't work nearly as hard as she used to.
    Ana used _____ .

Superlatives (**the longest / the most enjoyable**, etc.)

Complete the conversations with the superlative. Use the words in parentheses, *in* or *of* if needed, and any other necessary words.

1. *A:* Is Brazil a big country?
   B: (big country / South America) Yes, it's _the biggest country in South America_ .

2. *A:* I hear that you had a bad storm in your area.
   B: (serious storm / the decade*) Yes, it was one _of the most serious storms_
   of the decade .

3. *A:* Pat is pretty busy, isn't she?
   B: (busy people) Yes, she's one _____ that I know.

4. *A:* Cory is a great friend, isn't he?
   B: (dependable friend) Yes, he's _____ I've ever had.

5. *A:* How old is Mark?
   B: (old child / his family) I'm not sure, but I know that he's _____
   _____ .

6. *A:* Is Brussels an expensive city?
   B: (expensive cities / Europe) Yes, it's one _____ .

7. *A:* Did your friends stay at a nice hotel?
   B: (nice hotel / the city) Yes, they stayed at _____ .

8. *A:* (famous person) Who is _____ you've ever met?
   B: Let me think. The governor, I guess.

9. *A:* Is spring a good time to visit Chile?
   B: (pleasant season / the year) Yes, I think it's _____ .

10. *A:* Is your local high school basketball team good?
    B: (good teams / the country) Yes, it's one _____ .

11. *A:* Which is safer, a train, a plane, or a bus?
    B: (safe form of transportation) Actually, I think the airplane is _____
    _____ that you can take.

12. *A:* Did you answer Question 3 on the test?
    B: (difficult questions) Yes, but it was one _____ on the test.

13. *A:* Did you do well in school?
    B: (bad students / the class) Actually, I was one _____
    _____ .

*decade: *period of 10 years*

Adjectives and Adverbs

Comparison and Superlatives

Complete the second sentence, keeping the same meaning.

1. I bought this notebook because it was the cheapest one.
   I bought this notebook because it was *cheaper* _____ than the others.

2. Jan is the hardest-working person in our office.
   Jan works *harder than* _____ the other people in our office.

3. Watching TV is the most boring activity I can think of.
   I can't think of an activity that's _____ .

4. Frank is the least athletic person I've ever met.
   I've never met anyone who's _____ .

5. This intersection is more dangerous than any other in the city.
   This is _____ the city.

6. That was the happiest day of my life.
   I've never been _____ I was on that day.

7. Buses are more crowded during rush hour than at any other time.
   Buses _____ during rush hour.

8. This vacation spot is the most peaceful place I've ever stayed at.
   I've never stayed at _____ this one.

9. Ahmed's grade* was the highest in the class.
   _____ than the other students' grades.

10. You're the funniest person I know.
    _____ the other people I know.

11. Stan doesn't travel as far to work as the other teachers.
    The other teachers _____ .

12. Parker Posie isn't as well known as Angelina Jolie.
    Angelina Jolie is _____ .

13. My experience yesterday was worse than any I've ever had.
    I had _____ my life yesterday.

14. A simple solution is often the best.
    _____ more complicated ones.

*grade: *points or letter mark (A, B, C) given by a teacher for a student's work in school*

Review of Comparisons and Superlatives

Complete the conversations. Use the words in parentheses in the correct form and any other necessary words.

1. *A:* Is the food in that restaurant good?

   B: (good restaurant) Yes, a lot of people think it's ___the best restaurant in___ town.

2. *A:* Why aren't you going to Hawaii with your friends?

   B: (much money) I don't have ___as much money as___ they do.

3. *A:* Why are you so tired tonight? It's not very late.

   B: (early) I probably got up ___earlier than___ you did today.

4. *A:* (rich person) Who is _____ the world?

   B: I'm not sure. It might be Bill Gates.

5. *A:* How is your dad doing after his accident?

   B: (badly) He's not doing _____ he was. He can walk normally now.

6. *A:* Why did David get a raise? I didn't get one.

   B: (hard) Maybe he works _____ you do.

7. *A:* Are you finished eating? Ready for dessert?

   B: (slowly) No, I eat _____ you do.

8. *A:* (big) Which country has a _____ population, China or India?

   B: (big population) Right now, China has _____ the world.

9. *A:* Would it be better to go to Thailand in the spring or the summer?

   B: (nice) In my opinion, summer isn't _____ spring there.

10. *A:* (easy) This computer game is hard. Don't you have an _____ one?

    B: (easy) No, that is _____ one that I have.

11. *A:* (badly) I did badly on the test, but Sheryl did _____ me.

    B: (much) Maybe she didn't study _____ you did.

12. *A:* (often) Ted doesn't come to see us _____ he used to.

    B: (busy) No, his job keeps him a lot _____ before.

13. *A:* (fast) Sorry I'm late. I got here _____ I could.

    B: (long) That's all right. We started the meeting without you. We couldn't wait any

    _____ .

Word Order 1: Verb + Object; Place and Time;
Word Order 2: Adverbs with the Verb

Put the words in parentheses in the correct order to make sentences.

1. (usually / for breakfast / during the week / don't / time / have)
   I _don't usually have time for breakfast during the week_ .

2. (his lunch / again / burned / probably / has)
   Pablo _____ .

3. (forgot / almost / last week / your birthday)
   I _____ .

4. (walk / a cane / can / only / with)
   Mr. Lee _____

   _____ .

5. (in the winter / Mrs. Conrad / abroad / usually / travel / don't)
   Mr. and _____ .

6. (hot chocolate / every morning / at her desk / likes to drink)
   Mona _____ .

7. (on the weekends / has / never / go hiking / time to)
   Hannah _____ .

8. (suit / new / a lot / like / your / and overcoat)
   I _____ .

9. (seldom / on Saturday / in her apartment / is)
   Sarah _____ .

10. (your glasses / forgot / last night / at my house)
    You _____ .

11. (definitely / on time / to work / will / get / next week)
    Ken _____ .

12. (play with / also / will / on the weekend / in a band / his friends)
    Ken _____ .

13. (always / but she / says she's / usually isn't / sorry,)
    Ana _____ .

14. (risky / hardly ever / anything / do)
    My parents _____ .

Still, yet, and already; Anymore / any longer / no longer

Look at the pictures of a street in a small town 10 years ago and today. Read the sentences about 10 years ago. Complete the sentences about today with *still* or *not . . . anymore*.

Main Street 10 years ago

Main Street today

1. There used to be a hotel on Main Street 10 years ago.
   There _isn't a hotel on Main Street anymore_ .

2. There was a hardware store on Main Street.
   There _is still a hardware store there_ .

3. There was a dry cleaner's.
   There _____ .

4. There were lots of cars on Main Street before.
   There _____ .

5. Teenagers used to ride their bikes on Main Street.
   Teenagers _____ .

6. We used to be able to go to the movies on Main Street.
   We _____ .

7. People had trouble parking downtown before.
   People _____ .

8. You could find something to read in town 10 years ago.
   You _____ .

9. It was hard to find something to eat on Main Street before.
   It _____ .

10. There were trees along Main Street 10 years ago.
    There _____ .

11. You could get a suit or dress dry-cleaned on Main Street 10 years ago.
    You _____ .

Adjectives and Adverbs

Even

Complete the passage with *if*, *even*, *even if*, or *even though*.

My friend Sylvia used to have insomnia.* She is 37, a bank teller, and married with two children. She couldn't fall asleep at night **1)** <u>*even though*</u> she worked hard every day and felt tired at night. She tried different solutions to cure her insomnia. She tried exercising before bedtime, but it was **2)** _____ harder for her to fall asleep after exercising.

Then she tried sleeping pills **3)** _____ she has never liked to take pills. They helped her fall asleep, but she felt tired the next day. Someone advised her to take a hot bath before going to bed. Unfortunately, that made her feel **4)** _____ less sleepy at bedtime.

I suspect* Sylvia was one of those people who can't relax when the day is over. **5)** _____ her body was always tired at the end of the day, her mind was very active. She worried a lot – about work, her family, the house, **6)** _____ the family's cat and dog. Sometimes she worried about people that she didn't **7)** _____ know!

When I saw her last week, Sylvia was doing surprisingly well, though. She was worrying less and sleeping much better. Before, she worried about everything. Now, somehow she realizes that worrying doesn't help things. "Whatever is going to happen will happen. I can't change it," she said to me. Now, **8)** _____ the telephone rings in the middle of the night, it doesn't wake her up. She sleeps very soundly* the whole night. Some nights, **9)** _____ she doesn't have to help her children with their homework, she **10)** _____ goes to bed before they do. And **11)** _____ she and her husband go out and come home late occasionally, she falls asleep as soon as her head hits the pillow. Her husband doesn't **12)** _____ have time to ask her about her schedule for the next day.

I am going to ask Sylvia how she solved her sleeping problem. I would like to know how she learned to worry less **13)** _____ I don't have trouble sleeping myself. **14)** _____ you worry too much, you might want to try Sylvia's solution, too.

Follow-up: Think of a problem that you tried unsuccessfully to solve in several different ways. Did you finally succeed in solving the problem? Explain on a separate piece of paper.

*insomnia: *inability to sleep*   *suspect: *to have an idea; to believe*   *soundly: *deeply, well*

Word order: Verbs, objects, and adverbs

Insert the words in parentheses into their correct positions in the sentence.

definitely tomorrow

1. Will you˄be on time? (tomorrow / definitely)

2. I can't find Sally's address. (still / on my laptop)

3. Maybe we don't have the address. (anymore / even)

4. I drink a glass of milk. (before bed / sometimes)

5. I drink coffee. (after 3:00 p.m. / never / at home)

6. Are you and your brothers at home? (tonight / all)

7. Sheila fell off a ladder. (at work / almost / yesterday)

8. Have you and Sam voted? (both / yet)

9. Kim won't be at work. (tomorrow / probably)

10. My children are late. (for dinner / hardly ever)

11. A child can understand this poem. (easily / even)

12. Have you taken out the garbage? (today / already)

13. We have heard from Ken. (in Miami / not / yet)

14. Can you give me a ride? (after work / home / still)

15. Bill and Sue are working. (at the bank / no longer / probably)

16. I want you to stop arguing. (both / right now)

17. Stan and Ted moved. (last month / to Houston / both)

18. Sally has gotten to work. (on time / always)

19. Are your parents in town, or have they gone back home? (still / already)

20. I can't remember his name, but I can picture his face. (still / anymore)

21. Did they say to meet them? (at the club / definitely / at 5:30)

22. This computer was cheaper. (even / last week / at another store)

Adjectives and Adverbs

Adjectives and Adverbs

Use your own ideas to complete the sentences about yourself.

1. I don't have as much _free time as I used to_ .
    I don't have as much _hair as my friend does_ .
    I don't have as much _money as I need to go to college_ .
    I don't have as much _____ .

2. Not even my best friend knows that _____ .

3. I don't _____ enough anymore.

4. The more I _____ ,
    the less I _____ .

5. I can't _____ as well as
    _____ .

6. The happiest day of my life was when I _____ .

7. I don't understand why people have less _____
    _____ .

8. My life is a lot more _____ .

9. As time goes by, I feel more and more worried about _____
    _____ .

10. Sometimes I feel that I am too _____ .

11. The sooner I _____
    _____ .

12. I can hardly _____ , but I can still
    _____ .

13. Even though I have _____
    _____ .

14. I wouldn't _____ even if
    _____ .

15. I usually feel much better if _____ .

16. A friend of mine eats twice as much _____ .

Although / though / even though / in spite of / despite

Complete the sentences, keeping the same meaning.

1. It was a cold day, but we went on a hike and enjoyed it.
    Even though *it was a cold day, we went on a hike and enjoyed it* .
    In spite of *the cold (weather), we went on a hike and enjoyed it* .
    It was a cold day. We went on a hike and enjoyed it , though.

2. She felt really sick, but my sister had to take care of my nephew.
    In spite of feeling _____ , _____
    _____ .

3. I didn't care for the lunch my aunt made, but I ate it anyway.
    Even though _____ ,
    _____ .

4. I wasn't very busy yesterday, but I forgot to go to the bank.
    _____ . _____ , though.

5. My sister had a flu shot,* but she still got the flu.
    Even though _____ .

6. Rick answered her angrily, but Angela didn't show any anger herself.
    Despite Rick's angry _____ .

7. I didn't have much money as a student, but I managed to graduate by working part-time.
    Although _____
    _____ .

8. I wasn't very hungry, but I went to a restaurant with my friends.
    _____ . _____ , though.

9. Ana is having problems with her teenagers, but she manages to stay in a good mood.
    Despite _____ , Ana
    _____ .

10. Despite wanting to visit Mongolia, Sandy only went to Beijing.
    Even though _____ .

11. It was a beautiful day, but I stayed inside to study.
    Although _____ .

12. Cal is having money problems. He bought a new shirt, though.
    In spite of _____ .

*flu shot: *vaccination against influenza (flu)*

Conjunctions and Prepositions

In case; Unless, As long as, Provided/providing

Complete the sentences, keeping the same meaning.

1. I won't be able to finish this job if no one helps me with it.

   I won't be able to finish this job unless *someone helps me with it* .

2. I'll make dinner for us, but only if you go to the store first.

   Provided *you go to the store first* , I'll make dinner for us.

3. You should take extra money along on your trip. You might need it in San Francisco.

   _____ in case _____ .

4. The Suarez teenagers can stay out late, but they have to call home to say where they are.

   _____ as long as _____ .

5. I'll go running in the morning if it's not raining.

   I'll _____ unless _____ .

6. Ted always leaves his phone number with the babysitter. She might need to contact him.

   _____ in case _____ .

7. You will get along with Angela, but be careful what you say to her.

   You _____ as long as _____ .

8. I can't go to the movies with you unless you pay for my ticket.

   _____ providing _____ .

9. Why don't you take your allergy* medicine along? You might need it.

   Why _____ in case _____ ?

10. My computer printer usually works well unless I've been using it too much.

    _____ if _____ .

11. I'll go to Hawaii with you if I have enough money.

    Provided _____ , I'll _____ .

12. I'm going to lend Tom the car if you don't need it.

    _____ unless _____ .

13. We went to the party a little early. We thought the hostess* might need some help.

    We _____ in case

    _____ .

14. I'm going to take these leftovers* home if you don't think you'll eat them.

    Unless _____ , I'm _____

    _____ .

*allergy: *an illness that results from eating certain foods or breathing or touching certain substances*   *hostess: *woman who receives others as guests in her home*   *leftovers: *food remaining from a previous meal*

In some of these sentences, *like*, *as*, *when*, or *since* are used incorrectly. Correct the sentences where necessary.

1. Sally doesn't go out much or see many people. She lives as a hermit.*

   She lives like a hermit.

2. Since you don't want to go shopping, I'll go alone.

   RIGHT

3. Most U.S. students are 18 as they graduate from high school.

   _____

4. Like you may have heard, Richard is now the director of his company.

   _____

5. The repairman arrived at 8 a.m. as he had promised.

   _____

6. As I was leaving the house, I realized I hadn't taken my sunglasses.

   _____

7. A lot of players get injured in sports as hockey and football.

   _____

8. As her coworkers, Pam has to pay for her own uniforms since the company doesn't provide them.

   _____

9. Don't tie the package that way. I'll show you – do it as this.

   _____

10. Selma works like a nurse, but she was trained to be a doctor in her country.

    _____

11. As usual, Tim spent his weekend on his hobbies, things as gardening and painting.

    _____

12. Since we're all hungry, let's sit down and eat. Sue can eat as she gets here.

    _____

13. My feet are really cold. They feel as ice.

    _____

14. The party didn't turn out like I expected, but it was a lot of fun anyway.

    _____

15. The phone rang as I was leaving the house. As I was in a hurry, I didn't answer it.

    _____

*hermit: *a person who lives alone apart from society, often for religious reasons*

Conjunctions and Prepositions

Like and as

Read the sayings and then read the situations. Write the letter of the situation that best illustrates each saying.

Sayings

_d_   1. It was like taking candy from a baby.

_____   2. It's like looking for a needle in a haystack.

_____   3. Like father, like son.

_____   4. Do as I say, not as I do.

_____   5. They are like two peas in a pod.*

_____   6. I took to it like a duck takes to water.

_____   7. When in Rome, do as the Romans do.

_____   8. There's no place like home.

Situations

   a. Somehow I wasn't surprised when I heard that Matthew was getting divorced again. They say his father's been married four times!

   b. You can't imagine how much Lisa looks and acts like her sister.

   c. I've never liked taking a long time to sit down for a meal, but on my vacation I went to France, where people do it every day. So I did it too!

✓ d. It was easy to sneak* a note to my friend during class. I just waited until the teacher turned his back to write on the board.

   e. Mehrad lived in many different countries as a diplomat and liked each one in different ways. But he enjoys living in his own country even more, now that he's returned.

   f. "Did you have any trouble getting used to the food in Guatemala?"   "Not at all. I loved it from the first bite."

   g. We'll never find your ring on the beach. It's too small, and the beach is too big.

   h. Abby, who's 15, wants to smoke with her friends. Her parents are really upset. They've told her she shouldn't smoke, even though they smoke themselves.

Follow-up: Think of your own situations to illustrate two of the sayings. See if your classmates can guess which saying your situation illustrates.

       *pod: *a long seed container that grows on some plants*   *sneak: *to do something secretly*

As (= at the same time) and as (= because); Like and as; Like / as if / as though

Circle the correct word(s).

1   George works as / like a massage therapist.

2.   As / As if you probably already know, Tim's getting married next month.

3.   What's wrong? You look as / as if you had just seen a ghost.

4.   The movie we saw last night didn't end as / as though I expected it to.

5.   As / Since I was turning the key to start my car, I heard a strange noise.

6.   Brendan felt foolish just as / when he finally realized his mistake.

7.   Like / As you probably know, Elena and Bruce have decided not to have children.

8.   Sandy looks as / like she's had a hard day at work.

9.   Since / As though you don't understand this, I'll explain it to you again.

10.   You have a sense of humor just as / like my Uncle Bill's.

11.   I don't know why the employees didn't do as / as if they were told.

12.   The baby's acting as / as though she's sick.

13.   I'm an adult. Please don't treat me as / as if I were a child.

14.   If you ask me, you should wear livelier colors like / as blue and red.

15.   Just as / like Amy got to work, her boss called her into his office.

16.   That new singer sounds a lot as / like a singer from a long time ago.

17.   Kathy speaks German as / as if she had grown up in Germany.

18.   When / As I finished the shopping, I called home for a ride.

19.   It smells as / as though someone is cooking fish.

20.   Emily spoke as / as if she were angry with me.

21.   The air got cooler and cooler as / just as we drove up the mountain.

22.   Gina came to see us last night. She was full of news, as / like usual.

23.   As / Like his brother, Cal has brown hair and blue eyes.

24.   I feel as / as if I'm coming down with a cold.

25.   It looks like / as it's going to rain outside.

Conjunctions and Prepositions

For, during, and while; By and until, By the time . . .

Complete the paragraph with *by*, *by the time*, *during*, *for*, *until*, or *while*.

I have a demanding* job and a wife and three children, so my days are very full and busy. I try to go to the health club after work two or three times 1) <u>*during*</u> the week to relax and relieve* stress. I exercise 2) _____ about an hour at the club before going home. 3) _____ I'm at the club, I try to work out* on the machines 4) _____ about 20 minutes and swim 5) _____ an equal amount of time. Sometimes the machines are all taken, so I run 6) _____ I'm waiting for a machine. I exercise 7) _____ I feel tired, and then I stop so that I don't overdo* it. Because I've been especially busy at work, I haven't gone to the club 8) _____ several days, and I miss the exercise a lot. I need it, but my family is very important to me, too.

My wife, Sally, decided not to go back to work 9) _____ the children start school. She stays home with the children and is very busy 10) _____ the day. She is usually exhausted 11) _____ I get home, so I try to give her a break. She relaxes 12) _____ I take care of the kids.

Since my children don't go to sleep 13) _____ 9:00 p.m., I have a little time to spend with them after I get home. As long as I get home 14) _____ 7:00, I can still eat dinner with my family and have time to play with the kids before they go to bed.

My wife and I don't go to bed 15) _____ around 10:30, so we have time together without the children, too. I have to get up 16) _____ 6:00 a.m. to get to work on time, so my day starts early. 17) _____ bedtime comes, I'm usually very tired and fall asleep fast. I try to stay up 18) _____ Sally is ready for bed, but sometimes I just fall asleep. When one of the kids needs something 19) _____ the night, it's usually Sally who gets up and takes care of them 20) _____ I go on sleeping. It's a busy life for both of us.

*demanding: *needing a lot of time or attention*   *relieve: *to make less bad*   *work out: *to exercise, especially with weights or on exercise machines*   *overdo: *to do something too hard or for too long*

Conjunctions and Prepositions

Use your own ideas to complete the sentences about yourself.

1. My life is good even though *it can sometimes be hard* .
   My life is good even though *I have to deal with difficult people in my work* .
   My life is good even though _____ .

2. In spite of some difficulties, my father _____ .

3. It's always good to have extra money in case _____ .

4. Some parents get angry unless their children _____ .

5. I am happy as long as _____ .

6. I will probably _____ next summer provided I _____
   _____ .

7. As my parents get older, they _____ .

8. Like most people, I don't like _____ .

9. Sometimes I feel as though _____ .

10. I depend on my friends a lot. They _____ ,
    though.

11. I will probably continue learning English unless _____
    _____ .

12. Providing that I learn English well, _____ .

13. One day last week I felt as if _____ .

14. My friends will all do well in life as long as _____ .

15. There are days when I just don't feel like _____ .

16. The next time I go shopping, I'm going to _____
    in case _____ .

17. For a long time now, I've wanted _____ .

18. I'll probably live here until _____ .

19. By the time I turn 65, I will _____ .

20. I don't like to be interrupted while _____ or during
    _____ .

Prepositions

At/on/in (Time); On time and in time, At the end and in the end

Write *at*, *on*, or *in*. Leave the space empty if the sentence is already complete.

1. a. Many Americans get married __*in*__ June.

    b. My brother got married _____ June 4, 1993.

    c. Not many people get married _____ 10:00 _____ night, but it's possible.

    d. _____ the end, I guess people can get married any time they want to.

2. a. I don't like to travel _____ the winter.

    b. I took a wonderful trip with friends _____ last August.

    c. We got home happy and tired _____ Labor Day, which is a holiday for us.

3. a. Experts say it's better to exercise _____ the beginning of the day rather than _____ the end.

    b. Do you have more energy _____ the morning, _____ the afternoon, or _____ night?

    c. Would you like to play tennis _____ this Saturday?

4. a. A lot of diseases have been eradicated* _____ the last 100 years.

    b. Many diseases that were a problem _____ the past are no longer a problem.

    c. A lot of medical research is being done on AIDS and cancer _____ this time.

    d. _____ the 19th century and before, people died of diseases that are seldom fatal* today.

    e. Of course, other serious new diseases like AIDS may emerge _____ the future.

5. a. Scott isn't very punctual.* He seldom gets to work _____ time.

    b. Did you get to work _____ time for your meeting?

    c. We got stuck* in traffic, so we didn't make it to the wedding _____ time for the beginning. We were just a little late.

6. a. _____ first I didn't understand Julia's question, but she made it clear _____ the end.

    b. In my office, we usually have less work _____ Christmas.

    c. Our boss might give us a bonus* _____ six months if the company makes a profit.

7. a. I can't think of that man's name _____ the moment.

    b. I'm sure I'll think of it _____ a minute.

    c. My memory is usually excellent. I can learn a poem by heart _____ a few minutes.

---

*eradicate: *to put an end to*   *fatal: *causing death*   *punctual: *not late*   *stuck (past participle of *stick*): *not able to move*   *bonus: *extra money given as a present or reward*

Complete the sentences. Use *in*, *at*, or *on*.

1. Mary didn't come to work __on__ her bike today. I saw her __in__ a car.

2. Poor Claudia is sick _____ bed. She's staying _____ home today.

3. Would you rather spend your free time _____ a concert or _____ a movie?

4. I was _____ a meeting from 8:00 till 11:00 yesterday morning.

5. I don't think I'll have time to eat lunch _____ my usual restaurant before my trip, so I'll just buy something and eat it _____ the plane tonight.

6. Did you stay _____ your cousin's place _____ the mountains or her place _____ the coast?

7. I have a friend who would rather be _____ work than _____ home. Imagine!

8. My father met your boss _____ a party _____ a ship.

9. Is it safer for a child to sit _____ the back of the car or _____ the front?

10. Don't you want to write your return address _____ the top left corner of the envelope before I mail the letter?

11. I had to stand _____ a line for 20 minutes _____ the post office to buy stamps.

12. It's starting to rain. Let's wait _____ the post office until it stops.

13. Chicago isn't _____ the Mississippi River; it's _____ Lake Michigan.

14. Did you see that strange name "Kalamazoo" _____ a map or _____ a book?

15. Jason lives _____ a busy street _____ the first floor, so his place is noisy.

16. George doesn't have time to work now that he's _____ law school.

17. I never got used to driving _____ the left when I was in Tokyo.

18. Glen couldn't find his watch because he had put it _____ a small table _____ the corner. He didn't see it there later when he was looking for it.

19. We had agreed to meet _____ the bookstore, but I found Tim waiting _____ the entrance.

20. It's nice of your cousin to ask us to stay, but I'd rather not sleep _____ the floor. I'd rather pay to stay _____ a hotel.

21. Are you related to all the people _____ this photo?

22. There wasn't much _____ the menu that I cared to eat.

To/at/in/into; In/at/on (Other Uses)

Write *at*, *in*, *into*, *on*, or *to*. Leave the space blank if the sentence is complete.

1. *A:* Did you get __to__ work late this morning?
   B: Yes, but I had to drive __in__ the rain and __at__ 20 miles per hour most of the way.

2. *A:* *(husband to wife in a hotel)* Can we get _____ our room yet? I need to lie down.
   B: No, we arrived _____ the hotel too early. Let's sit outside _____ the sun while we wait.

3. *A:* Are the factory workers still _____ strike?
   B: No, I saw _____ TV that they had settled the strike and gone back _____ work.

4. *A:* Did you see Mark and Jan when you were _____ vacation in Seattle?
   B: No, they were _____ a tour of Canada.

5. *A:* Did you drive _____ the office today?
   B: No, I came by bus. I can get _____ the bus right in front of the building, so it's easy.

6. *A:* I wish we could go back _____ home now. I'm tired of traveling.
   B: Let's go back _____ the hotel. You'll feel better after you rest awhile.

7. *A:* Did Frank go to Miami _____ business again?
   B: No, he took his wife on vacation. She's never been _____ Florida.

8. *A:* The teacher said we had to write our essays _____ our own words and _____ pencil.
   B: I can't believe we can't use our computers. _____ my opinion, that's just silly.

9. *A:* You look tired this morning. Did you get _____ home late last night?
   B: No, but I went _____ bed pretty late.

10. *A:* I'm sorry I broke your cell phone, but I didn't do it _____ purpose.
    B: That's all right. I saw a new model _____ TV that I want to get.

11. *A:* Do you think Amy is _____ love with Rob?
    B: Yes. There are a few things about him that bother her, but _____ the whole, she thinks he's great.

12. *A:* Claudia's only 18. Isn't that too young to get married?
    B: No, people can get married without their parents' permission _____ the age of 18 in this state.

13. *A:* What time does our plane arrive _____ Miami?
    B: Around 9:00 p.m. I'll be so glad to get _____ home. I'm tired of sleeping _____ strange beds.

Prepositions

In/at/on (Other Uses); By

EXERCISE
150

UNITS
124–125

Write *at*, *by*, *in*, *on*, *to*, or *with*.

1. I went to work __*in*__ a taxi because I was too tired to go __*on*__ foot.

2. Don't be angry with Ted. He took your book _____ accident. He didn't do it _____ purpose.

3. My father was supposed to be _____ the 5:00 train, but he didn't come until after 6:00. I waited _____ my car for an hour.

4. This sweater was made _____ great care _____ my aunt.

5. They are presenting a play _____ the American writer Arthur Miller _____ the radio this week.

6. A man _____ a mustache is waiting for you _____ your office. Shall I send him _____ the conference room?

7. By the time you get to the airport and through security, traveling _____ plane sometimes takes as much time as it does _____ car.

8. Will you please stop talking? It's hard for me to talk _____ the phone when you're trying to talk to me at the same time.

9. Let's go downtown _____ my car. It takes too long _____ bus.

10. This picture was obviously taken _____ a professional _____ a very good camera.

11. World Cup Soccer is watched _____ TV or listened to _____ the radio _____ millions of people.

12. Do you pay cash or _____ credit card when you shop? I've heard you can sometimes get things cheaper _____ 4 or 5 percent if you pay cash. I personally pay for everything _____ check so that I have a record.

13. They say that today the world is warmer _____ a few degrees Celsius than it was previously. _____ my opinion, something needs to be done, but I don't know how or _____ whom.

14. I saw a store that was _____ fire at the mall. _____ the radio, they said it might have been started _____ someone who used to work there.

15. *A:* Shall we take my car _____ the movies?
    B: No. Let's go _____ the bus. It's safer _____ icy weather.

16. *A:* Do you _____ chance know if Peru is a good place _____ a vacation?
    B: It's marvelous, especially if you go _____ a tour of the Mayan ruins.

Prepositions

When do you do these things? Which would you never do? Which might you do under certain circumstances? Use your own ideas to answer the questions.

1. brush your teeth: *I usually brush my teeth in the morning after breakfast and at night before going to bed.*

2. open a can with a knife: *I might open a can with a knife on a camping trip if I forgot a can opener.*

3. decide not to study before an exam: _____
   _____

4. be alone on a dark street at 3:00 a.m.: _____
   _____

5. hide from someone in the back of a car: _____
   _____

6. not arrive at school/work on time: _____
   _____

7. go on vacation by yourself: _____
   _____

8. wait an hour for a friend on the corner in the rain: _____
   _____

9. visit a sick relative in the hospital: _____
   _____

10. spend all your money at the beginning of the month: _____
    _____

11. wish you lived in another century (in the past or in the future): _____
    _____

12. do in five minutes something that needs an hour: _____
    _____

13. work on weekends: _____
    _____

14. get up during the night: _____
    _____

Prepositions

Answer the questions in your own words.

1. How would you go to these places? (in your own car? on foot? by bicycle? in a taxi? on the train? on a bus? by plane or boat? on a motorcycle that you rented?) Why?
   - to a small village in the mountains on a sunny day *I would go to a small village in the mountains on a sunny day on a bus because I don't have a car.*
   - to a restaurant five blocks away on a dark night in the rain _____
     _____
   - downtown in the morning in bad weather _____
     _____
   - to another country on vacation _____
     _____

2. Which can you arrive at late? Which should you be on time for? Which are good to get to early?
   - class *I should arrive on time for class.*
   - work _____
   - a wedding _____
   - a concert _____
   - a meeting with your boss or teacher _____
   - a café to meet a friend _____

3. Think of a person you didn't get along with at first but who you liked in the end. Explain.
   _____
   _____

4. Sometimes we do something on purpose, but later we pretend it happened by accident or by chance. Describe an example.
   _____
   _____

5. Have you ever been injured in an accident? Have you ever been hurt by someone on purpose or by accident? Explain.
   _____
   _____

6. In your opinion, at what age should a person do these things?
   - live on their own: *Many people are ready to live on their own at 18.*
     _____
   - get married: _____
   - have children: _____
   - stop working: _____

Complete the conversations using the words in parentheses. Add necessary prepositions. Use the simple present tense.

1. *A:* Why was the train late?

   B: (I / not / know / the reason / the delay) _I don't know the reason for the delay._

2. *A:* Do you think soccer is becoming more popular in the U.S.?

   B: (there / be / an increase / the number of fans) _Yes, there is an increase in the_ _number of fans_ _____ every year.

3. *A:* Will it take long to repair the damage from the storm?

   B: (the damage / many buildings / be / extensive) Yes. _____
   _____

4. *A:* Why are Jim and Dave arguing?

   B: (the cause / the argument / not be / clear to me) _____
   _____

5. *A:* What do the flood victims* need?

   B: (there / be / an urgent need / blankets and clothes) _____
   _____

6. *A:* The city has been discussing the water problem for years, hasn't it?

   B: (it / not / be / easy to find a solution / that problem) Yes. _____
   _____

7. *A:* Why didn't you answer Question 17? You left it blank.

   B: (I / not / know / the answer / that question) _____
   _____

8. *A:* Why doesn't Roger see his father more often? They live in the same town.

   B: (his relationship / his father / not / be / very good) _____
   _____

9. *A:* I never know which twin is Sara and which one is Sue.

   B: Yes. (it / be / hard / to tell / the difference / them) _____
   _____

10. *A:* Should I get a laptop or a desktop computer?

    B: (the advantage / a laptop / is / its portability) _____
    _____

*victim: *a person hurt or killed in a disaster, a crime, etc.*

Adjective + Preposition 1

Complete the sentences, keeping the same meaning. Use an appropriate preposition after the adjective. Sometimes you need a pronoun.

1. Are you angry because I shouted at you?
   Are you mad _at me for shouting at you_ ?

2. I stupidly answered the question without thinking.
   It _was_ stupid _of me to answer the question without thinking_ .

3. Did his answer surprise you?
   Were you surprised _at/by his answer_ ?

4. Does the price of gas shock you?
   _____ shocked _____ ?

5. It showed generosity when you gave your brother the last piece of cake.
   It _____ generous _____ .

6. Does Max's progress in English impress you?
   _____ impressed _____ ?

7. Linda has no interest in school.
   _____ bored _____ .

8. His knowledge of insects astonishes me.
   _____ astonished _____ .

9. We found the service at the restaurant disappointing.
   We _____ disappointed _____ .

10. It hurts that Jerry forgot to invite me to his party.
    _____ upset _____ .

11. Does my solution to the problem satisfy you?
    _____ satisfied _____ ?

12. The little girl's song pleased everyone.
    _____ pleased _____ .

13. George shouldn't have spent all his money on a new shirt.
    It _____ silly _____ .

14. Sally politely shook hands with everyone in the room.
    It _____ polite _____ .

Adjective + Preposition 2

Complete the sentences. Use an adjective from the box and the correct preposition.

ashamed	aware	capable	~~famous~~	jealous
responsible	sure	tired	worried	

1. You'll love this restaurant. It is _famous for_ its desserts.

2. You told your father a lie? You should be _____ yourself!

3. An only child can be very _____ a new baby in the family.

4. There is no way Ed could have cheated. I am _____ that.

5. Who is mainly _____ children's characters – their parents or their teachers?

6. Green beans again?! I am so _____ eating green beans.

7. I had to wait for the store to open. I wasn't _____ their new schedule.

8. Hannah's a great athlete, but I don't think she's _____ running 800 meters in two minutes.

9. What's wrong? You look _____ something.

different	engaged	married	proud
short	similar	suspicious	tolerant

10. You won't recognize Stanley now. He looks a lot _____ before.

11. I can't pay you back this week. I'm a little _____ money right now.

12. Make sure you get to class on time. Ms. Timms isn't very _____ students who come late.

13. I don't trust Sam. I'm _____ the reason he gave for needing money.

14. It's hard to tell Jean's writing from her sister's. They are _____ each other.

15. The Chens have four children who all have scholarships to good colleges. I bet they are very _____ them.

16. *A:* How long has Sylvia been _____ Glen?

    B: They're not married. She is only _____ him.

Verb + Preposition 1: **to** and **at**

**Complete the sentences. Use the appropriate form of a verb from the box + *at, to, about,
for*, or *of*, if necessary.**

apologize	describe	explain	~~look~~
shout	talk	thank	throw

1. Why are you _looking at_ me like that? I didn't do anything.

2. Claudia _____ me from the back of the bus yesterday to say hello.
    Her loud voice made people look at us.

3. *(on the phone)* May I _____ Mr. Smith, please?

4. The police asked Kevin to _____ them the man he saw.

5. Brandon couldn't _____ me on the phone how to fix my computer.

6. Would you please _____ this bread _____
    the birds?

7. Freddie _____ his aunt _____ forgetting her
    invitation to dinner last week.

8. I can't _____ you enough _____ giving me
    a ride home in the rain.

aim	answer	ask	call	explain
glance	laugh	point	stare	

9. Can you _____ the meaning of "articulate" _____ me?

10. I don't know the answer to your question. _____ your mother.

11. You're not a very good shot. You'll never hit the target unless you _____
    it more carefully.

12. I don't think this situation is funny at all. What are you _____ ?

13. When students don't _____ the teacher in class, it often means they
    don't understand the question.

14. Don't _____ your finger _____ me. That's rude!

15. Sarah was sitting in the library and _____ a book, but I know she was
    thinking about something else.

16. Why don't you _____ the bus schedule for a minute while I
    _____ the station?

Prepositions

Verb + Preposition 2: about/for/of/after

Complete the sentences. Use a preposition and a pronoun (*it*, *him*, *them*, etc.).

1. There are many homeless people here, but the city doesn't know what to do ___*about them*___ .

2. An old lady disappeared last night. The police are searching _____ .

3. I used to leave my kids with my mother, but she can't take care _____ anymore.

4. Stop worrying about the storm. There's nothing we can do _____ .

5. Let's not buy carrots anymore. I really don't care _____ .

6. Your problem's serious. I think we need to have a long discussion _____ .

7. My divorce is a sad subject for me. I wish you'd stop talking _____ .

8. There is one more piece of cake. Would you care _____ ?

9. Clothes are very important to many people. Teenagers care a lot _____ .

10. Many jobs are advertised on the Internet. Imagine how many people must apply

    _____ .

11. *A:* Why didn't you give Carl his books back?

    B: He didn't ask me _____ .

12. *A:* What time is the wedding?

    B: At 4:00 p.m. If we leave _____ by 3:00 p.m., we'll get there in time.

13. I can't leave home. The repairman hasn't come yet. I'm waiting _____ to fix the air conditioning.

14. *A:* Why wasn't Joe accepted at Harvard or Yale? He's brilliant.

    B: He didn't apply _____ .

15. Old Mr. Brown lives alone. He has no one to look _____ .

16. Gloria is sitting somewhere in the concert hall. Help me look _____ .

17. Scott studied modern art for 10 years. He knows everything _____ .

18. *A:* Did the workers on strike get more money?

    B: I'm not sure, but I know they asked _____ .

19. *A:* Your little brother's cute. Do you ever take care _____ ?

    B: Yes. I look _____ and my sister when my parents go out.

20. *A:* Have you found your keys yet?

    B: No, I'm still looking _____ .

Verb + Preposition 3: **about** and **of**;
Verb + Preposition 4: **of/for/from/on**

Complete the sentences, keeping the same meanings. Use *about*, *for*, *from*, *of*, or *on*.
Make any necessary changes.

1. My dream is to go to Egypt someday.

   I dream _of going to Egypt_____ someday.

2. That man looks like someone I know.

   That man reminds _____ .

3. Amy complained that her new car cost too much.

   _____ that she'd paid too much _____ .

4. Hannah hasn't written or called me since last summer.

   I haven't heard _____
   _____ .

5. More Americans have heart disease, but cancer kills more.

   More Americans suffer _____
   _____ , but more die _____ cancer.

6. My brother might move to San Francisco.

   My brother is thinking _____
   _____ .

7. My roommate said that I was lazy.

   My roommate accused _____
   _____ .

8. That child eats almost nothing besides cereal and milk.

   _____ practically lives
   _____ .

9. This sunscreen will keep you from getting a sunburn.

   _____ will protect
   your skin _____ the sun.

10. The radio usually tells people when there are serious weather conditions.

    The radio usually warns _____
    _____ .

11. I can't remember the name of that restaurant.

    I can't think _____
    _____ .

12. Don't say that your problems are my fault.

    Don't blame _____
    _____ problems.

13. I might be able to buy the bike; it depends on the price.

    I might be able to buy the bike; it depends
    _____ it costs.

14. I love it when people say my hair looks nice.

    I love it when people compliment _____
    _____ my hair.

15. I can't believe you don't know who Pablo Neruda is.

    I can't believe you've never heard _____
    _____ .

Prepositions

Verb + Preposition 5: **in/into/with/to/on**

Choose the best completion.

1. Your confidence will increase if you believe __c__ .
   a. yourself   b. in you   c. in yourself

2. With all this noise, it's hard for me to concentrate _____ .
   a. myself   b. on this book   c. at this book

3. Fortunately, no one was hurt when the two cars collided _____ .
   a. with each other   b. each other   c. with themselves

4. When he was learning to drive, Chris drove _____ .
   a. in a stop sign   b. into a stop sign   c. on a stop sign

5. For moderate* exercise, many people prefer swimming _____ .
   a. to more strenuous* activities   b. more than running   c. to run or hike in hot weather

6. My company supplies employees _____ .
   a. with giving them uniforms   b. in uniforms   c. with uniforms

7. I doubt Angela will ever succeed _____ snoring.*
   a. to get Bob to stop   b. with stopping Bob from   c. in getting Bob to stop

8. For this recipe, you need to cut the onion _____ .
   a. into small pieces   b. to small pieces   c. in one big piece

9. I offered to help, but Sandy insisted _____ .
   a. to do it by herself   b. in going to the movies alone   c. on changing the tire alone

10. My language skills aren't good enough to translate this letter _____ .
    a. in German   b. to Korean   c. into Arabic

11. The restaurant serves many things, but they specialize _____ Greek food.
    a. in   b. with   c. into

12. The Careys have no idea when their house was broken _____ .
    a. in   b. in to   c. into

13. Bad things sometimes happen _____ .
    a. with nice people   b. on nice people   c. to nice people

14. I don't like to spend money _____ .
    a. in foolish things   b. on foolish things   c. with foolish things

15. Mr. Grimes doesn't believe _____ .
    a. to work hard   b. on working hard   c. in working hard

16. To be fair, Mother divided the chocolate _____ .
    a. to two big pieces   b. to all her children   c. into equal parts

---

*moderate: *neither too much nor too little*   *strenuous: *needing a lot of energy*   *snore: *to breathe in a noisy way while sleeping*

Prepositions

Use your own ideas to complete the sentences about yourself.

1. I spend most of my money on _clothes (OR rent and food OR my kids)_ .
   I spend most of my money on _____ .

2. I don't believe in _lending people money (OR ghosts)_ .
   I don't believe in _____ .

3. I made a mistake. It was silly of me to _____ .

4. I can always rely on _____ when
   _____ .

5. There are many things I'd like to do in my life. I sometimes dream of _____
   _____ .

6. I am different from _____ because
   _____ .

7. I don't normally care for _____ .

8. It would make me very happy to hear from _____ because
   _____ .

9. I wish the government would do something about _____
   _____ .

10. I sometimes get upset about some people's attitude toward _____
    _____ .

11. I am fond of _____ , but I'm not very good at
    _____ .

12. I love having discussions about _____ because
    _____ .

13. Sometimes people compliment me on _____ .

14. When foreigners come to my country, I usually warn them about _____
    _____ .

15. I hate it when people complain about _____ .

16. I should probably apologize to _____ for _____
    _____ .

Phrasal Verbs

Phrasal Verbs 1 Introduction

Which endings complete the sentence in a logical way? Check (✓) one, two, or three endings.

1. If you are trapped* in a building,
   - ____ a. you will probably run around looking for a window to look out of.
   - ____ b. the first thing you'll worry about is how to turn on the heat.
   - ✓ c. you'll probably try to find a way to get out.
   - ____ d. you'll send an e-mail to a friend asking to be woken up in two hours.

2. If you hear that robbers got away with $50,000 from a bank, it probably means that
   - ____ a. their get-away car broke down.
   - ____ b. they waited 20 minutes for a bus after the robbery and got on it.
   - ____ c. the robbery was successful and they weren't caught.
   - ____ d. they did not drive off in an orderly manner.
   - ____ e. they got away from the police.

3. If you can get by in English,
   - ____ a. you can probably fill out a simple form in the language.
   - ____ b. it means you probably kept up with your English homework in school.
   - ____ c. it means you'll get along fine in France.
   - ____ d. you don't have to give back the English dictionary you borrowed.

4. If you run out of money next month,
   - ____ a. you might ask a friend who borrowed money to pay you back.
   - ____ b. it will be good if you get along well with your parents.
   - ____ c. you might have to go back to living at home with your parents.
   - ____ d. it will be easy to keep up with your rent.
   - ____ e. you should try to get by without eating until your next paycheck.

5. If you are looking forward to going to a party next weekend, you
   - ____ a. probably get along well with the people who will be there.
   - ____ b. probably read the invitation and threw it away immediately.
   - ____ c. will run away if you see the hostess* coming your way this week.
   - ____ d. will send the invitation back to the hostess unopened.

*trapped: *unable to escape from (something)*   *hostess: *woman who receives others as guests in her home*

Phrasal Verbs 2: **in/out**

Complete each sentence using the correct form of a verb from the box + *in, into, out*, or *out of*.

drop	eat	fit	~~hand~~	join	let	plug	walk

1. If I don't __*hand in*__ my report today, the boss will be mad at me.

2. The teacher _____ the room at the end of class before I could ask him my question.

3. "Do your roommates ever cook meals at home?"   "No, they _____ almost all the time."

4. All the other people in the club were excellent photographers, but I'm just a beginner. I didn't feel that I _____ .

5. I need to charge my cell phone. Where can I _____ it _____ ?

6. Tim started taking classes in August, but he _____ school two months later because of his job.

7. You left the door open again. You're _____ flies _____ the house.

8. We had a wonderful discussion in class this morning. The whole class _____ , so I got to hear everyone's opinion.

check	drop	fill	get	go	leave	lock	move

9. The doctor will be with you soon. Please _____ these forms while you're waiting.

10. I'm supposed to take care of my nieces tonight, but I'll see if I can _____ it. I'd much rather go to the movies with you.

11. The ATM outside the bank isn't working. We'll have to _____ the bank to get money.

12. Should we call Chris to say we're coming to visit, or can we just _____ ?

13. I'd rather you told the police what happened, and don't _____ any important details. They'll want to know everything.

14. "Have you met the new neighbors yet?"   "No, they just _____ . I haven't even seen them yet."

15. I _____ myself _____ of the house last night. I knew as soon as the door closed that I'd left my keys inside.

16. We have to _____ the hotel by noon tomorrow. What will we do until our flight leaves at 6:00 p.m.?

EXERCISE
163

Phrasal Verbs

Phrasal Verbs 3: **out**

UNIT
136

Complete each sentence using the correct form of a verb from the box + *out*.

~~carry~~	find	hand	point	put	try	turn	work

1. "Have the police solved the crime yet?" "No, they have just begun __*carrying out*__ their investigation."

2. How can I _____ who is responsible for hiring people in this company?

3. Stan had trouble in the beginning, but he has _____ to be a really good employee.

4. Thanks for _____ the mistakes in my essay. Now that I see them, I can fix them.

5. I don't feel very fit these days. It's because I haven't _____ at the gym for several weeks.

6. "Did we leave the lights on downstairs?" "No, I _____ them _____ before I came upstairs."

7. "Did you get a copy of the new schedule that the bus company was _____ last week?" "Yes, and I got one for you too."

8. Let's go to the Internet café to _____ the printer you're thinking of buying. Then we'll know for sure if you like it.

blow	carry	figure	go	put	run	work	work

9. Have the firefighters been able to _____ the forest fire that started last week?

10. "Are your brother and his wife still separated?" "No, they have _____ things _____ and gotten back together."

11. This is the first time I've _____ of gas. There's nowhere to buy any – we'll just have to walk home.

12. "Will my telephone still work if the lights have _____?" "It should work – but you'll have to call in the dark!"

13. How is your new job _____? Well, I hope.

14. There were so many candles on the birthday cake that it was hard for old Mr. Simms to _____ them all _____ at one time.

15. The police officer apologized for asking so many questions. He said he was just _____ his orders.

16. This map is hard for me to _____ . Which way is north?

Phrasal Verbs

Phrasal Verbs 4, 5: **on/off** (1, 2)

EXERCISE
164

UNITS
137–138

Complete the conversation between 16-year-old Ben and his mother. Use an appropriate form of a verb from the box in each blank.

~~be~~ call drop go have lay put put rip take try

Ben: I 1) _am_ off to the store to get clothes for the new school year.

Mom: Do you want me to 2) _____ you off at the mall on my way to do my errands?

Ben: No, thanks. Mac's giving me a ride. And I'm not going to the mall. They charge too much. They 3) _____ you off. I can get the same clothes cheaper at a discount store.*

Mom: OK, but doesn't Mac have to work this morning?

Ben: No, he hasn't worked in over two weeks. He was 4) _____ off last month.

Mom: Sorry to hear that. Anyway, promise me that you will 5) _____ on everything before you buy it. The last time, you brought home clothes that didn't fit.

Ben: But I hate 6) _____ on clothes and then 7) _____ them off a dozen times. I'll just get the same sizes that I 8) _____ on right now.

Mom: Do what you want. I'm not going to 9) _____ on making your decisions. You're old enough to make them.

Ben: Will you be home for my basketball game this afternoon?

Mom: I thought the game had been 10) _____ off.

Ben: No, the coaches just decided to 11) _____ off playing until later in the afternoon when it's cooler. We play at 5:00.

doze get go go hold see take turn

Mom: I'll be there, then. Don't forget we're going to the airport to 12) _____ your grandmother off on her trip to Ireland tonight. I think her flight's at 10:00.

Ben: I'll be so tired by then that I'll probably 13) _____ off in the car. My alarm 14) _____ off at 5:00 this morning, and I couldn't get back to sleep. What's 15) _____ on with Dad? I hardly see him anymore. Is he going to the airport, too?

Mom: No, two people at work are on vacation, and he's had to 16) _____ on their work. He won't be home until late. Well, I'd better 17) _____ on with my day, or I'll never finish. 18) _____ off the TV before you leave, OK?

Ben: 19) _____ on a minute, Mom. Can you give me some money for shopping?

Mom: I thought you were going to use the money your grandparents gave you for your birthday.

*discount store: *store where prices are lower than in most other stores*

Answer the questions with your own words, using phrasal verbs when you can.

1. What are you looking forward to in the next two weeks or in the next two years?
   I'm looking forward to having a guest from Germany this weekend.

   _____

2. What kind of people do you get along with / not get along with? _____
   _____

3. When is it better to drop out of school rather than go on studying? _____
   _____

4. If two friends were moving into their first apartment, what present might you give them and
   why? _____
   _____

5. Have you ever been ripped off when you bought something? What did you buy? Why did you
   feel ripped off? _____
   _____

6. Everyone has run out of money, gas, or milk for the baby some time. But a person can also
   run out of patience. When do you run out of patience? _____
   _____

7. When was the last time someone told you off? Why did it happen? _____
   _____

8. Bad things that happen often bring something good later on. Write about a bad experience
   that turned out well in the end. _____
   _____

9. What advice would you give to these people?
   a. Someone who has trouble keeping up with their work at the office.
      If you have trouble keeping up with your work, you could talk to your boss
      about getting some help.

      If you have trouble keeping up with your work, _____
      _____

   b. Someone who has been locked out of their house.
      If you have _____
      _____

   c. Someone who has just found out they inherited a lot of money.
      _____
      _____

Phrasal Verbs

Phrasal Verbs 6: **up/down**

EXERCISE
166

UNIT
139

Complete the paragraphs using appropriate forms of the verbs in the box + **up** or **down**.

THEN

NOW

| cut | pick | put | slow | take | ~~tear~~ | write |

Wilson Elementary School looks a lot better now. The small temporary classroom was
1) _torn down_ , and the school has 2) _____ the dead trees. The school
has 3) _____ the old sign and 4) _____ an attractive new one
in its place. The litter has 5) _____ . Now when cars approach the school,
the drivers 6) _____ and stop to let the children cross the street. The crossing
guard is 7) _____ the license number of a driver who ignored the children
waiting to cross.

| break | burn | close | cut | let | turn |

Mom and Pop have not been lucky. When Big Discounts opened nearby, Mom and Pop
started losing business. Then one day their refrigerator 8) _____ , and
they had to pay for expensive repairs and lots of spoiled food. They tried to
9) _____ on expenses by keeping fewer products in the store, but then
customers felt 10) _____ when they couldn't find what they had come in for.
Someone offered to buy the small grocery, but Mom and Pop 11) _____ their
offer. Not long after, there was a fire. The store didn't 12) _____ completely, but
Mom and Pop finally had to 13) _____ it _____ . They just
couldn't afford to keep running the small business because they were losing so many customers.

Phrasal Verbs

Phrasal Verbs 7: **up** (1)

Complete the paragraphs with phrasal verbs in the appropriate form. Use verbs from the boxes.

bring up	end up	give up	grow up	keep up	~~take up~~

A friend and I decided to **1)** _take up_ a new hobby – hiking in the mountains – but we
2) _____ deciding we would have to stop hiking together if we wanted to
remain friends. I'll tell you why.

Mark **3)** _____ in a big city doing everything fast, and that's how he hikes,
too. I was **4)** _____ in a small town by patient parents who did everything
slowly. The first time Mark and I went hiking together, he was far ahead of me after only
20 minutes. I just couldn't **5)** _____ with him, so I finally
6) _____ trying to and just walked slowly.

back up	back up	catch up	end up	show up	walk up

I thought I'd **7)** _____ with Mark at the top of the mountain, but halfway up,
I met Mark coming back down. He said, "Hurry up. We need to leave for the city soon,
or the traffic will be **8)** _____ for miles. Anyway, why are you so far behind me?"

I said something about a sore* ankle and continued climbing. Mark went back down. I knew
he'd be impatient, so I turned around after 20 more minutes. When I got to the parking lot,
I could see Mark waiting for me to **9)** _____ . The second he saw me, he
started to **10)** _____ the car so we could leave right away. I
11) _____ to the car and asked through the window, "What's the point of
going hiking together if we **12)** _____ hiking separately?"

give up	make up	take up

Mark said, "What are you talking about? This was a great hike, but I think hiking
13) _____ too much time. I'm too busy to spend time sitting around waiting
for you. Come on, get in."

Do you see why we **14)** _____ hiking together? They say the world is
15) _____ of two kinds of people: those who concentrate on goals and others
who see life as a journey. I guess it takes both kinds of people for the world to work right.

*sore: *painful and uncomfortable*

Phrasal Verbs

Phrasal Verbs 8: up (2)

EXERCISE

168

UNIT
141

Rewrite the sentences. Replace the underlined part(s) with the correct form of a verb in the box + *up*.

blow	cheer	hold	put	save	split

1. Marge has felt so sad since her husband died. What can we do <u>to make her feel happier</u>?
   What can we do to cheer her up?

2. The enemy <u>destroyed</u> the bridge into town <u>with a bomb</u>.

3. How can you <u>tolerate</u> such rude behavior?

4. We were <u>delayed</u> by an accident on the highway. Sorry we're late.

5. Rose and her husband <u>are getting divorced</u> after 20 years of marriage.

6. Phil and Sue <u>are putting money in the bank</u> regularly because they want to buy a car.

beat	bring	clear	come	make	mix

7. When you talk to the boss, never <u>introduce</u> our salaries <u>into the conversation</u>. He doesn't like to talk about money.

8. That little boy <u>was hit and badly hurt</u> by older boys at the school.

9. Don't believe what Ana said about her brother. She <u>invented</u> the whole thing.

10. We couldn't play our match until it <u>stopped raining and the sun came out</u>.

11. My brother and I look a lot alike. People are always <u>mistaking us for each other</u>.

12. Let's ask George for advice. He always <u>thinks of</u> something useful to say.

EXERCISE
169

Phrasal Verbs

Phrasal Verbs 9: **away/back**

UNIT
142

Which endings complete the sentence in a logical way? Check (✓) one or two endings.

1. If you give your poetry book away,
   - ____ a. you expect to get it back.
   - ✓ b. you don't expect to get it back.
   - ____ c. it will probably come back to you.

2. A teenager who runs away from home
   - ____ a. will probably come back home soon.
   - ____ b. should try to keep away from dangerous places.
   - ____ c. may stay away for a long time.

3. When children finish playing with their toys,
   - ____ a. they should put the toys away.
   - ____ b. they should try to get away with leaving the toys on the floor.
   - ____ c. they should throw the toys away.

4. If a friend doesn't say hello back to you at a party,
   - ____ a. you should stay away from that person in the future.
   - ____ b. you should take back any presents you've given them.
   - ____ c. you should try to remember if perhaps you haven't paid them back money you owe them.
   - ____ d. you should probably just walk away and try again next time.

5. If a friend you left a phone message for doesn't get back to you in two days,
   - ____ a. you should look away the next time you see them.
   - ____ b. it could mean they're out of town and haven't come back yet.
   - ____ c. you should never leave them another phone message.

6. If an old person you don't know smiles at you on the bus,
   - ____ a. you should smile back.
   - ____ b. you should look away.
   - ____ c. you should keep away from that person if you see them again.

Phrasal Verbs 6, 7, 8, 9

Write your own answers to these questions.

1. What's the best way to cheer someone up if they've failed an exam? _To cheer them up._
   I could offer to study with them before the next exam.
   _____
   _____

2. We all have things that bother us. What is something that really bothers you – that you can't
   put up with at all? _____
   _____

3. Will you / Do you / Did you bring up your children the same way you were brought up by
   your parents? Explain. _____
   _____
   _____

4. What behavior do boys sometimes get away with that girls don't?
   _____
   _____

5. Imagine that you're at a party with friends and someone you don't like shows up. What do
   you do? _____
   _____

6. How do you feel about tearing down old historic buildings to build new modern ones? Is
   there a way to keep up traditions while becoming more modern? _____
   _____
   _____

7. What things would you cut down on if you suddenly had much less money? What things
   would be hard to give up?
   _____
   _____
   _____

8. If someone asked you to do something that you felt was wrong, would you turn them down?
   How could you get out of doing it without hurting them or letting them down? What words
   would you say?
   _____
   _____
   _____

Answer Key to Exercises

In some exercises, you have to use your own ideas to write answers. The answer key says "Answers will vary." If possible, check your answers for these exercises with someone who speaks English well.

EXERCISE 1

3. 'm making (am making) a salad
4. are painting the bedrooms
5. 's taking (is taking) a shower
6. 'm not having (am not having) a good time
7. 's studying (is studying) law
8. 's improving (is improving) all the time
9. isn't rising ('s not rising; is not rising)
10. isn't snowing ('s not snowing; is not snowing)
11. 'm beginning (am beginning) to like
12. 's growing (is growing) very fast
13. 're reading (are reading) the same one

EXERCISE 2

2. he usually exercises
3. She does her homework (She does it) in the library
4. takes care of him
5. she teaches math
6. I don't drink (do not drink) coffee
7. She doesn't like (does not like) him
8. Does he live
9. doesn't look (does not look) very happy
10. she never agrees
11. Do you promise
12. I refuse to give
13. She doesn't apologize (does not apologize)
14. He doesn't do (does not do) anything at home

EXERCISE 3

3. They usually work 10 hours a day.
4. Bob cooks the food, and Laura serves the customers.
5. Bob isn't cooking (is not cooking) today.
6. Laura isn't serving (is not serving) customers today.
7. Every day after school the children go to the restaurant.
8. They usually do their homework in the kitchen.
9. They aren't doing ('re not; are not doing) homework now.
10. They're spending (They are spending) time with their parents now.
11. Everyone looks happy.
12. Sometimes they hike in the hills on Mondays.
13. They aren't hiking (They're not hiking; They are not hiking) this afternoon.
14. Today they're playing (they are playing) tennis together.
15. Grandma usually visits the family on Mondays.
16. Today she's sitting (she is sitting) and watching the tennis game.

EXERCISE 4

2. 'm making (am making); need
3. Do; see; are; looking
4. is; think
5. Are; having; love; Are; enjoying
6. always does; promises
7. 'm beginning (am beginning); always asks
8. is thinking; likes

9. does; mean; depends; has
10. belongs; contains
11. don't realize (do not realize); 're being (are being)
12. Are; using; 'm eating (am eating)

EXERCISE 5

3. I didn't have (did not have) time to visit my parents last night.
4. Did you see the sunset last night?
5. The baby didn't eat (did not eat) all her breakfast this morning.
6. Were you on time for work yesterday?
7. My friends didn't get (did not get) a good price for their house last month.
8. You spent too much money on your last haircut.
9. Amy lost her ring, but I found it yesterday.
10. Did anyone get hurt in the accident yesterday morning?
11. Were you happy to see Claudia again last week?
12. We didn't have (did not have) enough money to get tickets for last night's concert.
13. How did Ann catch a cold?
14. Did you forget our teacher's name again?
15. Sam didn't do (did not do) anything wrong.
16. The book cost a lot, but I bought it anyway.
17. Rose went to that restaurant three times and ordered the same thing.

EXERCISE 6

2. rained; didn't rain (did not rain); is; 's snowing (is snowing); looks
3. 'm reading (am reading); 'm going (am going); Do; want
4. 's visiting (is visiting); took
5. 's studying (is studying); isn't ('s not; is not)
6. Did; go; 's taking care of (is taking care of); didn't see (did not see)
7. Did; happen; had

EXERCISE 7

4. They weren't taking (were not taking) a cooking class the last time I saw them.
5. He wasn't exercising (was not exercising) a lot the last time I talked to him.
6. You didn't want (did not want) to change jobs the last time I saw you.
7. She wasn't making (was not making) commercials for TV the last time I talked to her.
8. He wasn't having (was not having) trouble at work the last time I spoke to him.
9. You weren't talking (were not talking) about adopting a baby the last time I talked to you.
10. You weren't working (were not working) at home two days a week the last time I saw you.
11. They weren't having (were not having) problems the last time I spoke to them.

12. You weren't thinking (were not thinking) of moving to Toronto the last time I talked to you.
13. You didn't know (did not know) a lot of people in the city the last time I talked to you.
14. He wasn't trying (was not trying) to lose weight the last time I spoke to him.

EXERCISE 8

3. happened
4. didn't see (did not see)
5. slowed
6. stopped
7. didn't notice (did not notice)
8. was talking
9. was sitting
10. turned
11. drove
12. was crossing
13. tried
14. was
15. hit
16. were moving
17. got out
18. checked
19. spoke
20. had
21. arrived
22. made
23. happened
24. was; thinking

EXERCISE 9

3. When did you leave the house
4. What were you doing at 10:00 last night?
5. What do we need from the store?
6. Why are you so nervous?
7. Where were your glasses?
8. When does the mail carrier come?
9. Where did you find my keys?
10. Who are you talking to on the phone?
11. Why are you being so difficult today?
12. How did the thieves get into the school?

EXERCISE 10

Answers will vary.

EXERCISE 11

4. I've gotten (I have gotten)
5. Have you ever been
6. we've gone (we have gone)
7. Have you ever ridden
8. I've ever played (I have ever played)
9. I haven't seen (have not seen)
10. He hasn't come (has not come)
11. Have you ever failed
12. I haven't ever written (have never written)
13. I haven't tried (have not tried)
14. 've ever read (have ever read)
15. he's lost (he has lost)

EXERCISE 12

3. haven't seen (have not seen)
4. had
5. *RIGHT*
6. *RIGHT*
7. *RIGHT*
8. ate
9. *RIGHT*
10. *RIGHT*
11. grew up
12. has designed
13. had
14. *RIGHT*
15. had
16. built
17. *RIGHT*
18. didn't remember
19. wrote
20. *RIGHT*

EXERCISE 13

4. we haven't taken (have not taken)
5. people have gone
6. I've known (I have known)
7. I haven't paid (have not paid)
8. it broke down
9. I haven't driven (have not driven)
10. I haven't eaten (have not eaten)
11. didn't grow up (did not grow up)
12. they've made (they have made)
13. they didn't get (did not get)
14. I rode
15. they haven't arrested (have not arrested)
16. I haven't met (have not met)
17. she's been (she has been)
18. it's been (it has been)
19. haven't eaten (have not eaten)
20. saw

EXERCISE 14

3. 've been driving (have been driving) for three hours
4. Have you been watching TV all night?
5. I've/We've been taking (I/We have been taking) dance lessons
6. How long have you and Sam been staying in a hotel?
7. Have you been doing exercises for a long time?
8. 's been spending (has been spending) a lot of time
9. I've been exercising (I have been exercising) and eating less
10. How long has Sue been working in Australia?
11. 've been swimming (have been swimming)

EXERCISE 15

2. *B:* He's written (He has written) six letters so far.
3. *A:* How long have you been doing your homework?
   B: I've been studying (I have been studying) since breakfast.
4. *A:* How much money has Sonia spent today?
   B: She's spent (She has spent) $300 already.
5. *A:* How long have Joe and Ina been dancing?
   B: They've been dancing (They have been dancing) all evening.

6. *A:* How many times have you played cards this week?
   B: I've played (I have played) three times.
7. *A:* How many rooms has he painted today?
   B: He's finished (He has finished) three rooms.

EXERCISE 16

3. have you delivered
4. we haven't eaten (have not eaten)
5. have you been working (have you worked)
6. Has your wife; worked
7. He's (He has); told
8. has your father been selling (sold)
9. I've (I have); known
10. has your sister been trying
11. they've been (they have been)
12. I haven't seen (have not seen)
13. have you gotten
14. they've been playing (they have been playing)

EXERCISE 17

2. b; c
3. b; d
4. c; e
5. a; c
6. e

EXERCISE 18

A.

3. since I went to the doctor's
4. for ages
5. since the year before last
6. for about 10 years
7. two or three years ago

B.

2. How long have you been sick
3. When did you get sick
4. How long has your brother been traveling in Asia
5. How long has it been since you got this job
6. When did you get glasses

EXERCISE 19

3. She'd been (She had been) away for several years.
   We had a long talk.
4. I'd worked (I had worked) very hard all day.
   I didn't brush (did not brush) my teeth before bed.
5. Everyone was happy for them.
   They'd known (They had known) each other for seven years.
6. It was difficult for him.
   He'd never done (He had never done) it before.
7. Linda had gone to bed early.
   The doorbell didn't wake (did not wake) her.
8. We hadn't talked (had not talked) to each other for ages.
   We spent an hour talking about old times.
9. Mike had eaten something before the movie.
   He didn't order anything.

EXERCISE 20

3. He'd been sitting (He had been sitting) in traffic for two hours.
4. she was studying for a test

5. they'd been having (they had been having) an argument
6. he was watering flowers in the garden
7. She'd been swimming (She had been swimming) all afternoon.
8. I was talking on my cell phone.
9. she'd been hoping (she had been hoping) for a girl (*or* she was hoping for a girl)
10. 'd been losing (had been losing) money for months
11. it was raining hard a minute ago
12. 'd been expecting (had been expecting) it for months
13. 'd been traveling (had been traveling) abroad for three months

EXERCISE 21

3. 'd been buying (had been buying) tickets for years
4. haven't been feeling (have not been feeling) well since lunchtime
5. hadn't eaten (had not eaten) anything all day
6. 've been looking (have been looking) at a computer screen for hours
7. 've been having (have been having) a good time here
8. 've/'d been wanting (have/had been wanting) to see it for a long time
9. 's never been (has never been) there before
10. 'd given (had given) her an injection
11. 've been asking (have been asking) for something sweet

EXERCISE 22

1. d. went to see
    e. stopped crying
    f. 'd been having (had been having) (*or* 'd had *or* had had)
    g. has not woken up
    h. have been sleeping (have slept)
2. a. was swimming
    b. was having; enjoying
    c. 'd been swimming (had been swimming) (*or* 'd swum *or* had swum)
    d. was
    e. told
    f. was
    g. 'd paid (had paid); was (*or* 'd been *or* had been)
    h. haven't gone (have not gone)

EXERCISE 23

3. I used to have a nice big one
4. she was having trouble with her car
5. I used to run and play basketball
6. I was taking a nap.
7. wasn't paying (was not paying) attention
8. He used to pay attention
9. I didn't use to celebrate it
10. were celebrating their victory
11. I was working on a project

EXERCISE 24

Answers will vary.

EXERCISE 25

3. you're meeting (you are meeting)
4. you're calling (you are calling)
5. the director is coming

6. a writer is helping
7. I'm not typing (I am not typing)
8. the dinner begins
9. you speak
10. the dinner doesn't end (does not end)
11. Am I getting
12. Are you picking up
13. Who is ordering
14. You aren't getting (You're not getting; You are not getting)
15. I'm picking up (I am picking up)
16. The dry cleaner closes
17. I'm leaving (I am leaving)
18. You're practicing (You are practicing)
19. a computer technician is coming
20. you're going (you are going)
21. A driver is picking
22. it doesn't end (does not end)
23. the driver is coming back
24. is my wife getting
25. She's bringing (She is bringing)

EXERCISE 26

3. are you going to stay
4. He was going to visit
5. He's going to have
6. you were going to help
7. it's not going to be
8. I'm not going to quit
9. They're going to go
10. are we going to fix
11. They were going to take
12. I was going to sell
13. are we going to eat

EXERCISE 27

4. I'll ask (I will ask)
5. will disturb
6. Shall I get
7. it'll be (it will be)
8. will it cost
9. Will you do
10. will you call
11. we'll need (we will need)
12. shall we have
13. it won't rain (will not rain)

EXERCISE 28

3. are going to move
4. 'll come (will come)
5. aren't going to get together ('re not going to get together; are not going to get together)
6. 're going to stop (are going to stop)
7. 'll buy (will buy)
8. They're going to have (They are going to have)
9. 'll make (will make)
10. 'm going to go (am going to go)
11. aren't going to get ('re not going to get; are not going to get)
12. *A:* Will you speak
    B: I'll do (I will do)

13. *A:* Are you going to visit
    B: I'm going to have (I am going to have)
14. 'll carry (will carry)

EXERCISE 29

2. is going to quit
3. won't come
4. 'm coming
5. will pay
6. is going to rain
7. is going to burn
8. is playing
9. is coming
10. won't have
11. are going to arrive
12. won't tell
13. *A:* is
    B: are taking
14. won't make
15. are learning
16. will ask

EXERCISE 30

2. a. Greg will be making breakfast.
   b. Debbie will be giving her baby a bath.
   c. They won't have eaten (will not have eaten) breakfast yet.
3. a. They'll be eating (They will be eating) breakfast.
   b. The baby will have finished her bath.
   c. Greg won't have left (will not have left) for work yet.
4. a. Greg will have left for work.
   b. Debbie will have finished eating breakfast.
   c. Debbie will be feeding the baby.
5. a. The baby will be taking a nap.
   b. Debbie will be cleaning the house.
   c. The baby will have had her breakfast.
6. a. They'll be taking (They will be taking) a walk together.
   b. The baby will be riding in a stroller.
   c. They won't have gotten (will not have gotten) back home.
7. a. They will have returned from their walk.
   b. Debbie will be watching TV.
   c. The baby will be playing on the floor.

EXERCISE 31

4. stops
5. go
6. finds out
7. don't get (do not get)
8. reaches
9. saves
10. won't paint (will not paint)
11. moves
12. decide
13. 'll regret (will regret)
14. hurry
15. apply
16. apologizes
17. grow up
18. happens
19. won't bother (will not bother)
20. will call

EXERCISE 32

Answers will vary.

EXERCISE 33

3. be able to
4. could; be able to
5. could; could
6. be able to; can
7. be able to
8. could
9. can; Can
10. was able to
11. be able to; can
12. were able to
13. could; could
14. were able to
15. been able to

EXERCISE 34

3. could have
4. could have taken
5. could want
6. couldn't have asked
7. couldn't get
8. could break down
9. could have called
10. could have applied
11. could be
12. couldn't have gone
13. could have lost
14. could understand
15. could have eaten
16. can put

EXERCISE 35

2. could have bought
3. couldn't speak; can have
4. could hear
5. could have stayed
6. could mean
7. can't use
8. hasn't been able to find
9. Were you able to find
10. Can you do
11. was able to get
12. could have borrowed
13. couldn't understand
14. was finally able to
15. won't be able to
16. hasn't been able to
17. Could you
18. could understand

EXERCISE 36

4. must go to church
5. must not be here
6. must not be running well these days
7. must have gotten divorced
8. must be bothering him
9. must not have been at work last Friday
10. must have been thinking about something else
11. must not have been listening to me last night

12. must not be the right street
13. must not have heard me correctly
14. must be thinking about her date tonight

EXERCISE 37

3. be able to lend
4. could be
5. could have lent
6. must have borrowed
7. could have been (could be)
8. can't be (cannot be)
9. be able to fix
10. could fall asleep
11. must have picked up
12. must not have checked
13. must be
14. be able to attend
15. couldn't have copied (could not have copied)
16. can't be (cannot be)

EXERCISE 38

2. 2: may have forgotten it at school
3. 1: might miss her boyfriend
   2: She may have had an argument with her father.
4. 1: might be worried about something
   2: He may have eaten a lot for lunch.
5. 1: might be doing something else tonight
   2: She may have forgotten about the party.
6. 1: might be at the mechanic's
   2: may have sold his car
7. 1: might not have seen the other car
   2: She may not have been concentrating on her driving.
8. 1: They might have gone shopping for food.
   2: They may be at the doctor's.

EXERCISE 39

Answers may vary. Possible answers:
2. be calling (be trying to call)
3. eat
4. have remembered
5. be babysitting
6. be able
7. be mowing (be cutting)
8. buy
9. be waiting
10. slip (fall)
11. be able to
12. go; stay
13. have been feeling

EXERCISE 40

Answers will vary.

EXERCISE 41

3. *RIGHT*
4. don't have to buy (do not have to buy)
5. must not use
6. *RIGHT*
7. *RIGHT*
8. don't have to work (do not have to work)
9. *RIGHT*
10. don't have to take (do not have to take)

11. Do I have to work
12. *RIGHT*
13. Did Cal and Lena have to move
14. *RIGHT*
15. *RIGHT*
16. had to take

EXERCISE 42

4. should have bought
5. should get
6. should be working; shouldn't be (should not be) taking
7. should have been studying
8. should have been
9. shouldn't have (should not have)
10. shouldn't have been talking (should not have been talking)
11. should have returned
12. should think
13. shouldn't be watching (should not be watching); should be working
14. should have been paying

EXERCISE 43

3. try to walk without crutches
4. that he (Jerry) drink a lot of milk to make his bones strong
5. call him every day to get the homework
6. be given aspirin
7. that he (Jerry) not walk on his leg for three days
8. that he (Jerry) stay in the hospital longer

EXERCISE 44

A.
3. had better
4. should
5. had better
6. had better
7. should
8. should
9. should
10. had better

B.
2. bought
3. It's time we did something
4. It's time we went
5. It's time you were more
6. It's time we had

EXERCISE 45

1. c. will make his life easier
   d. would be safer
   e. won't buy (will not buy) a new car
2. a. will all have a chance
   b. would be happy
   c. wouldn't be (would not be) happy
   d. will probably get good jobs
3. a. wouldn't feel (would not feel) guilty
   b. won't quit (will not quit)
   c. wouldn't continue (would not continue) working
   d. will go to work
   e. would be a solution

EXERCISE 46

3. I don't have to take
4. suggested I relax
5. recommended I take
6. Can I do
7. That would be
8. Could you come over
9. My husband has to work
10. I would be
11. Should I come
12. I had better call
13. Could I take
14. time they spent
15. should put

EXERCISE 47

Answers will vary.

EXERCISE 48

3. he would be efficient
4. he knew where things were
5. people would work harder
6. if he answered questions clearly
7. he didn't tell (did not tell) different stories to different people (*or* if he told the same stories to everybody)
8. we could go home on time
9. the meetings didn't last (did not last) two hours
10. we wouldn't get (would not get) confused
11. if we felt secure about our jobs (if everybody felt secure about their jobs)
12. Frank wasn't/weren't (was not / were not) a terrible boss (*or* if Frank was/were a better boss)

EXERCISE 49

3. he worked in an office
4. wasn't/weren't raining (was not raining / were not raining) outside right now
5. wish they could afford a new car
6. wishes he lived near the ocean
7. wishes he owned a car
8. wishes she had only one cat
9. wish they didn't have (did not have) to get up so early
10. wasn't/weren't (was not / were not) so expensive

EXERCISE 50

3. If it hadn't been (had not been) a stormy day, the tourists would have gone swimming.
4. If she had been in class, she would have heard the teacher's announcement.
5. If he hadn't gotten (had not gotten) up late, he would have eaten breakfast.
6. If they had been at home, they would have received the package yesterday.
7. If she hadn't been (had not been) on her bike, she would have bought her groceries yesterday.
8. If he had been able to find his dictionary, he would have looked up the new word.
9. If I hadn't forgotten, I would have called you.
10. If we had known about it, we would have gone to Joe's party.

EXERCISE 51

2. wasn't/weren't (was not / were not) angry at me;
   hadn't told (had not told) other people her secret
3. had accepted it; I wish we were eating dinner
   there now
4. hadn't said (had not said) it; wasn't/weren't (was not /
   were not) so sensitive all the time
5. had told me; didn't live (did not live) so far away
6. I wish I hadn't spent (had not spent) so much money
   on my car.; I wish I could afford to spend time in the
   mountains.
7. was/were nicer today; I wish I had brought my
   umbrella this morning
8. he had had more time to think about it; wishes he
   didn't have to make (did not have to make) decisions
   so quickly all the time
9. I wish I was/were able to go.; I wish I had saved
   money this past year.

EXERCISE 52

4. Todd wishes he had studied . . .
5. *RIGHT*
6. Kim wishes she liked . . .
7. . . . I hope you have . . . (. . . I wish you a nice time.)
8. *RIGHT*
9. I wish you would stop talking . . .
10. . . . I hope it continues . . .
11. I wish I didn't have to go (did not have to go) . . .
12. I wish my alarm clock wasn't/weren't (was not / were
    not) so loud. . . .
13. *RIGHT*
14. . . . I wish we could have spent . . .
15. *RIGHT*
16. . . . I wish I had thought about it more.
17. I wish there were . . .
18. *RIGHT*

EXERCISE 53

Answers will vary.

EXERCISE 54

2. Mrs. Chen's dog was killed
3. are elections held
4. Mary was fired
5. Flights are sometimes canceled
6. I was accused
7. was your sweater made
8. isn't known (is not known)
9. the accident was caused
10. Was the first satellite sent
11. The letter *v* isn't pronounced (is not pronounced)
12. were baseball games canceled
13. Many houses are damaged
14. my camera wasn't stolen (was not stolen)
15. we were warned
16. is this thing used
17. were you taken

EXERCISE 55

2. have been injured
3. be paid
4. 's been cleaned (has been cleaned) for weeks
5. 's going to be built (is going to be built) next year
6. had been invented
7. be found
8. be washed
9. were being criticized
10. have been called
11. have been delivered
12. has been used
13. are needed

EXERCISE 56

3. worked
4. was asked
5. agreed
6. came
7. left
8. hasn't been paid (has not been paid)
9. has complained
10. has been done
11. asked
12. was refused
13. had to miss
14. was
15. hired
16. promised (had promised)
17. has been taking (took)
18. asked to be reimbursed
19. had been treated
20. will never be promoted
21. are given
22. wants to quit
23. doesn't want (does not want) to be given
24. leaves
25. has been contacted
26. might be offered
27. accept

EXERCISE 57

3. was born
4. Were we told
5. being treated
6. are you paid
7. *RIGHT*
8. was offered (has been offered)
9. *RIGHT*
10. doesn't get used (does not get used; isn't used; 's not
    used; is not used)
11. being criticized
12. *RIGHT*
13. being helped
14. *RIGHT*
15. has been offered (was offered, got offered)
16. getting invited

EXERCISE 58

2. b
3. f
4. a
5. c
6. g
7. e
8. j
9. h
10. l

11. i
12. m
13. k

EXERCISE 59

3. get our telephone number changed
4. gets her hair done
5. had her luggage searched
6. have my teeth cleaned
7. have the prescription delivered
8. get his house cleaned
9. get your car fixed
10. have a solar water heater installed
11. having the brakes checked
12. get my blood tested

EXERCISE 60

Answers will vary.

EXERCISE 61

3. said (that) he had to go to Toronto
4. He said (that) he didn't need (did not need); he's/he'd
   already read (he has/had already read) it
5. He said (that) his son was going to paint his house
   for him.
6. He said (that) his family is doing well.
7. He said (that) his father was (had been) sick, but (that)
   he was doing much better now.
8. He said (that) he really enjoyed (had really enjoyed)
   your cookies.
9. He said (that) he'd see (he would see) us next Saturday.

EXERCISE 62

3. (that) I like (liked) her accent
4. him to take it easy and relax
5. them (that) Charlie has (had) just bought a house
6. me to please wait until he was free
7. (that) I'd have to help out (I would have to help out)
   more at home
8. (that) he's been (he'd been) too busy
9. me not to tell anyone what she said
10. (that) I didn't have to bring (did not have to bring)
    a present

EXERCISE 63

2. isn't (is not) very responsible about money."
3. "He often spends money on himself instead of on me
   and the children."
4. don't tell (do not tell) your brother about our
   conversation."
5. "Don't worry (Do not worry). I won't say (will not say)
   anything to him."
6. "Speak to him honestly; don't get (do not get) angry
   while you're (you are) discussing these matters."
7. "Your anger will make him less likely to talk openly."
8. "I'll try (I will try) to follow your advice."

EXERCISE 64

3. she always cut her hair herself; she didn't cut (did
   not cut)
4. he always ate a very small breakfast, but he ate
5. she was taking the bus to work Thursday morning,
   but she drove her

6. he didn't know (did not know) how to play a musical
   instrument, but he was playing

Follow-up: Answers will vary.

EXERCISE 65

4. people came (to your party)?
5. have they had it (their house)?
6. did you miss it (the bus)?
7. was it (this road) built?
8. birthday present are you looking for?
9. forgot their notebook?
10. isn't she (Zoe) going to take it (her test)?
11. car did he (Jack) buy?
12. didn't she (Helen) say hello (to you this morning)?
13. (money) does she earn?
14. won't he return your calls (them)?

EXERCISE 66

3. How long have you had this car?
4. Why didn't you go to work yesterday?
5. What are the children listening to?
6. When (What time) are you getting up (are you going
   to get up) tomorrow?
7. How can I find a good used car?
8. Don't you feel well? (Aren't you feeling well?)
9. What's (What is) your brother doing?
10. How long ago did you come (When did you come) to
    this country?
11. How did you meet your husband?
12. Wasn't your teacher born in this country?
13. Where were these clothes made?
14. Who's (Who is) waiting to see me?

EXERCISE 67

2. where the magazines and newspapers are
3. how much that chicken weighs
4. if (whether) San Francisco is
5. when Shakespeare was born
6. why you got angry
7. what "diffident" means
8. where Ashgabat is
9. if (whether) I'll (I will) be sent
10. where my car keys are
11. how much a cell phone costs
12. when (what time) the next movie is
13. if Matt accepted the new job

EXERCISE 68

2. when she was going to hand in her homework.
3. The doctor asked me where I had pain.
4. We asked the hotel clerk what time the bus left for
   the airport.
5. The travel agent asked Mrs. White if (whether) she'd
   (she had) ever been to Hawaii.
6. The patient asked the dentist if (whether) it would
   hurt very much.
7. I asked my friend in Florida how the weather was there.
8. Sally asked her friend if (whether) she looked good
   in her new dress.
9. The students asked the teacher if (whether) they were
   going to have a party in December.
10. Barbara asked her father why she couldn't have (could
    not have) her own cell phone.

EXERCISE 69

A.
4. I haven't seen (have not seen) the new hospital
5. I shouldn't have (should not have) more cake
6. Rex likes to cook
7. Sue didn't buy (did not buy) Liz a present
8. Jeff had to leave town
9. My boss is on vacation

B.
2. his girlfriend will
3. have I
4. should you
5. is Lou's sister
6. do you
7. could I
8. my brother did
9. would any friend of mine

EXERCISE 70

Answers may vary. Possible answers:
4. You would? So would I. (I wouldn't.)
5. She does? So do I. (I don't.)
6. You haven't? I have. (Neither have I.)
7. She didn't? I did. (Neither did I.)
8. You can't? I can (Neither can I.)
9. You were? So was I. (I wasn't.)
10. You aren't? (You're not?) I am. (Neither am I.)
11. You should? So should I. (I don't have to.)
12. He does? So do I. (I don't.)
13. You did? So did I. (I didn't.)
14. You weren't? I was. (Neither was I.)
15. You wouldn't? I would. (Neither would I.)
16. You are? So am I. (I'm not.)
17. You don't? I do. (Neither do I.)
18. You haven't? I have. (Neither have I.)
19. You are? So am I. (I'm not.)
20. You do? So do I. (I don't.)

EXERCISE 71

2. I think so.
3. I don't think (do not think) so.
4. I'm afraid so.
5. I'm afraid not.
6. I guess so.
7. I guess not.
8. I'm afraid not.
9. I don't think (do not think) so.
10. I hope not.
11. I suppose so.
12. I suppose not.
13. I hope so.
14. I don't think (do not think) so.
15. I expect so.
16. I think so.

EXERCISE 72

3. can't you
4. isn't there
5. shouldn't it
6. am I
7. will you
8. didn't he
9. shall we
10. will she
11. do we
12. would you
13. has there
14. have we
15. wouldn't it
16. doesn't she
17. shall we
18. will they
19. don't they
20. aren't I

EXERCISE 73

Answers may vary. Possible answers:
4. Yes, I have. (No, I haven't.)
5. Yes, they are. (No, they're not.; No, they aren't.)
6. Yes, it does. (No, it doesn't.)
7. Yes, it has. (No, it hasn't.)
8. Yes, they do. (No, they don't.)
9. Yes, we should. (No, we shouldn't.)
10. Yes, I am. (No, I'm not.)
11. Yes, they should. (No, they shouldn't.)
12. Yes, they can. (No, they can't.)
13. Yes, it does. (No, it doesn't.)
14. Yes, I do. (No, I don't.)
15. Yes, I am. (No, I'm not.)
16. Yes, it would. (No, it wouldn't.)
17. Yes, there has. (No, there hasn't.)

EXERCISE 74

Answers will vary.

EXERCISE 75

2. interrupting
3. working in that
4. living alone
5. changing jobs
6. doing the shopping
7. watching a video
8. telling the same stories about
9. trying to change my husband's bad habits
10. lifting anything heavy
11. walking to work every
12. talking about you
13. living in a different country
14. getting caught
15. living without music
16. breaking into the house; stealing anything

EXERCISE 76

2. She; to get a raise at work
3. She; not to call him stupid again
4. She; to give him a ride home
5. He; to stay until the report was done
6. He; to visit his family this Christmas
7. not to buy a new car
8. She; to keep him in the house; didn't get a haircut
9. to give him five dollars (until he did his chores); not to know what she meant
10. He; to get the afternoon off
11. She; how to get to the airport (from there)

EXERCISE 77

4. Rob to get a job
5. your company to fire so many people
6. you to play the piano
7. me to become a doctor
8. to smoke in this building
9. the baby to stop crying
10. to break your glasses
11. me (to) make my decision
12. never to use anyone else's computer
13. me to pay for the book I lost
14. not to give my credit card number to a stranger on the phone
15. me leave the theater to use my cell phone
16. you look slim

EXERCISE 78

Answers may vary. Possible answers:
3. buying (getting, shopping for)
4. laughing (smiling)
5. working
6. putting (using)
7. to pick up (to get)
8. taking
9. to feel
10. meeting (being introduced to, talking to, seeing)
11. to drink
12. to stay (to remain, to be)
13. to discuss (to talk about)
14. carry (bring) (or to carry or to bring)
15. to inform (to tell)
16. asking (inviting)
17. to be cleaned (to be dry cleaned)
18. giving (handing); getting (receiving)
19. feeling

EXERCISE 79

2. a
3. c
4. c
5. c
6. b
7. a
8. c
9. b
10. c
11. a
12. c
13. b
14. c

EXERCISE 80

4. work at home than in an office
5. Would you rather stay
6. Puerto Rico to Las Vegas
7. called him
8. translated the letter
9. watching a movie at home to going out (to watch a movie at home rather than go out)
10. ate at home than in a restaurant
11. to do it now rather than later (doing it now to doing it later)

12. 'd rather not do (would rather not do)
13. went by yourself
14. going to a party to reading a book (to go to a party rather than read a book)
15. chat on the Internet than talk to someone in person

EXERCISE 81

2. making an effort
3. listening to native speakers
4. eating; going to bed
5. having dinner at my favorite restaurant tonight
6. running five miles every day
7. using public money for himself
8. making friends
9. going to Toronto next weekend
10. giving me directions
11. having to drive on snow and ice
12. taking a break; having a snack
13. seeing your brother
14. not returning his boss's phone calls
15. getting tickets for the game this late

EXERCISE 82

A.
3. sharing
4. living
5. remind
6. make
7. being
8. studying
9. drive
10. riding
11. taking
12. do
13. help
14. being

B.
2. used to
3. getting used to
4. used to
5. get used to
6. wasn't used to (was not used to)
7. aren't used to (are not used to)

EXERCISE 83

Answers may vary. Possible answers:
3. like going
4. of taking (of driving, of borrowing)
5. me for not getting (me for not being)
6. for forgetting (for not remembering)
7. to giving (to making)
8. on staying
9. in finding (in renting)
10. from getting
11. her from seeing (her from spending time with, her from going out with)
12. of going (of moving, of traveling)
13. them from doing (them from finishing)
14. on being (on getting)
15. her of being
16. him of lying
17. us for not going (to his wedding)
18. against buying

EXERCISE 84

3. apologizing to people
4. keeping this
5. watching TV
6. walking all the way to the market
7. calling Mary Jo
8. contacting my uncle
9. shopping
10. inviting Emily
11. working on his car
12. skiing in the winter and swimming in the summer
13. reading without glasses
14. buying bottled water
15. driving 50 miles; fishing

EXERCISE 85

A.

3. to visit
4. taking
5. getting
6. to decide
7. to go
8. leaving
9. studying
10. to know
11. to help
12. getting
13. feeling
14. to live
15. go
16. visiting
17. traveling

B.

1. have
2. turning
3. feeling
4. give
5. to invite
6. buying and preparing
7. eating
8. celebrating
9. get
10. not to bring
11. feel
12. to remember

EXERCISE 86

3. To try on some shoes.
4. For his driving test.
5. To have some lunch.
6. So that she wouldn't forget to stop at the bank.
7. So that he could buy groceries.
8. The opportunity to make more money.
9. So that they could spend the holiday with family.
10. To keep his neck warm.
11. So that he could go to college.
12. For a change.
13. So that I won't miss my bus.
14. For a trip to Finland.
15. The opportunity to talk to people.
16. For some privacy.
17. To keep us out.

18. To keep people away.
19. So that I can buy some stamps.
20. For relaxation.

EXERCISE 87

3. to see you on TV
4. to hear that Mike got out of the hospital
5. not to get the job I applied for (to find out that I didn't get [did not get] the job I applied for)
6. to meet your parents the other night
7. (of you) to go to bed with the doors unlocked ([of you] to leave the doors unlocked)
8. to rain
9. (of you) to quit your job before finding another one
10. to get the right answer
11. of my parents to punish my sister for something she didn't do (did not do)
12. to understand Milo because of his heavy accent
13. to have an accident
14. of Maria to offer the police officer money not to give her a speeding ticket

EXERCISE 88

2. to talk
3. in learning
4. to give
5. for forgetting (that I forgot, to have forgotten)
6. to have
7. of making
8. of asking
9. in getting
10. from being
11. from doing
12. to speaking
13. for not being
14. for doing (that I do)
15. to know
16. to interrupt
17. to waste
18. of wasting

Follow-up: Answers will vary.

EXERCISE 89

Answers may vary. Possible answers:

3. cry
4. fall (hurt herself)
5. leaking (coming, escaping)
6. knocking (pounding, banging)
7. use (say)
8. wearing (using, playing with)
9. eating (sitting)
10. talking
11. waiting (coming)
12. lose
13. cooking
14. talking
15. driving
16. shake
17. calling (*or* call)
18. buying (shopping for)
19. play
20. happening

EXERCISE 90

I had to wait a long time sitting in an uncomfortable chair. The doctor gave me a prescription for a painkiller, promising it would work fast. Not knowing that they would upset my stomach, I took the pills without food. Having left me at the doctor's earlier, my friend came to my house to see me last night. I woke up this morning feeling a little better. Having called work to say I wasn't going in, I ate and went back to bed.

EXERCISE 91

2. not buying a house when prices were low
3. to have come (to have been able to come) to your party
4. me to put the dishes away
5. to get married
6. of asking for another day off
7. us from turning around and driving the other way
8. trying to be friends with Pat
9. telling anyone your/my secret
10. not to have seen me
11. anyone knowing
12. her boyfriend of lying
13. seeing well without glasses
14. eat (eating) the last cookie

EXERCISE 92

Answers will vary.

EXERCISE 93

Answers will vary.

EXERCISE 94

Answers may vary. Possible answers:
2. a: Black pepper, lettuce, mushrooms, oil, olives, pieces of onion, salt, and tomatoes (OR a tomato)
   b: Butter, garlic, jam, lemon juice, and bananas
3. a: Experience, a good coach, strong arms and legs, healthy lungs, and time to practice
   b: Long hair, rainy weather, and an umbrella
4. a: baby clothes, a good doctor, help from relatives, information about vaccinations, money, and a spare room
   b: a truck or new living room furniture
5. a: clean water, enough sleep, exercise, fresh air, and good food
   b: Alcohol, a car, coffee, an expensive doctor, a hard job, stress, and tobacco
6. a: advice, dependability, a funny personality, good character, intelligence, and a person who knows how to listen
   b: Good behavior, a rich parent, and similarity to me

EXERCISE 95

2. a suggestion
3. helpful advice
4. Bad luck
5. bread
6. permission
7. a view
8. luggage; trips
9. foreign travel
10. rooms
11. room; big suitcases
12. good progress; hard work
13. hair
14. behavior
15. experience
16. information
17. an unusual experience

EXERCISE 96

4. a
5. –
6. the
7. –
8. some (–)
9. a
10. a
11. the
12. the
13. the
14. a
15. some (–)
16. –
17. –
18. a
19. –
20. some (–)
21. a
22. –
23. –
24. the
25. – (some)
26. the
27. the
28. the
29. the
30. the
31. –
32. the
33. – (some)
34. –
35. –
36. –
37. –
38. the

EXERCISE 97

A.
6. the
7. –
8. the
9. a
10. the (–)
11. the
12. –
13. –
14. –
15. the
16. the
17. a
18. the
19. the

20. a
21. the
22. –
23. the

B.
1. –
2. a
3. –
4. –
5. the
6. a
7. the
8. –
9. –
10. an
11. the
12. the
13. a
14. the
15. –
16. the
17. The
18. –
19. the
20. the
21. –
22. the
23. the
24. –
25. –
26. a
27. the
28. the
29. –
30. –
31. the
32. The
33. the

EXERCISE 98

2. the; the; the
3. –; –; –; the
4. –; –
5. –; –
6. –; –
7. the; –; –; –; the
8. the; –; the
9. –; –; the
10. –; –
11. –; the; –; –
12. –; the; –
13. –; –; –
14. –; –
15. the; the
16. –; –

EXERCISE 99

Answers may vary. Possible answers:
2. The Andes Mountains are; the Empire State Building.
3. O'Hare Airport in Chicago is; the Rhine-Main Airport in Frankfurt.
4. China has more people; the Czech Republic or Australia.
5. Mexico has a larger area than the Dominican Republic.
6. The north of Europe has a cooler climate than Southeast Asia.
7. The Far East has a larger population than the Middle East.
8. The Nile River is longer than the Mississippi River.
9. The Philippines has a larger population than Hawaii.
10. The Great Wall of China is longer than the Suez Canal.
11. The Giza Pyramids were more difficult to build than Buckingham Palace.
12. Princeton University is more famous than the University of California.
13. The Red Sea is warmer than the North Atlantic.
14. President Kennedy is more famous than the Queen of Jordan.
15. I would rather work for Sony than (for) the International Red Cross.

EXERCISE 100

3. There's (There is) a new species of bird at the zoo.
4. Where are your binoculars?
5. No news is good news
6. Fifty dollars is a lot of money for a book.
7. My only means of transportation is a bicycle. (A bicycle is my only means of transportation.)
8. Are those TV series new or old?
9. all politics is/are local
10. Math is a difficult subject for many students. (A difficult subject for many students is math.)
11. There are more police than firefighters in this city. (There are more police in this city than firefighters.)
12. These aren't (are not) my glasses.
13. Three years is a long time
14. Nice people aren't (are not) necessarily nice
15. A pair of shorts is sometimes more expensive
16. Physics is a difficult subject.; Electronics and economics are too.
17. Is $35,000 a big salary
18. People are generally good.

EXERCISE 101

4. a weekend athlete
5. ocean fish
6. money problems
7. an apple pie
8. cooking apples
9. salad plates
10. a 20-dollar bill (a $20 bill)
11. a 40-page chapter
12. a 100-year-old fire station
13. 42-cent stamps
14. a payday
15. a workday
16. a two-year contract
17. a 90-minute movie
18. a 60-minute program
19. a 14-day ocean cruise (a two-week ocean cruise)
20. nine-foot-high (ocean) waves
21. 10-year-old wedding pictures
22. a potato-chip factory worker
23. a 29-year-old heart doctor
24. hundred-dollar work shoes

EXERCISE 102

3. *RIGHT*
4. *RIGHT*
5. tonight's concert
6. *RIGHT*
7. girls' school
8. a half-day's pay (half a day's pay)
9. yesterday's leftovers
10. Glen and Lynn's house
11. *RIGHT*
12. June's husband's father (June's father-in-law)
13. city's parks
14. *RIGHT*
15. *RIGHT* (The world's population)
16. Pam and Phil's car
17. *RIGHT*
18. *RIGHT*
19. children's clothes
20. next week's baseball game
21. Mr. Thompson's secretary
22. the secretary's brother-in-law (the secretary's husband's brother)

EXERCISE 103

Corrections are underlined.

We would like to escape from ~~a~~ the cold weather at home in Minnesota, visit some pyramids in the area, spend some time at the beach, and practice Spanish. Of course, we'll eat new dishes and meet ~~the~~ new people, too. My friends think I am only interested in eating, but that opinion is very unfair. To me, the food in a new country is an important part of the culture of the country (OR part of the country's culture). It would be a terrible mistake to go to a foreign country and stay at fancy hotels and eat the same food as at home. While in Mexico, we plan to visit the Maya ruins at Chichen Itza. The ruins are located in the south of Mexico (OR in southern Mexico), near the Caribbean Sea. Today, we admire the skill of the ancient Maya in architecture, math, and astronomy. They built temples, pyramids, palaces, and observatories without metal tools. I especially want to see Kukulan, a 2,000-year-old pyramid and temple. The Maya developed an advanced civilization when much of the world was still living in primitive conditions.

Follow-up: Answers will vary.

EXERCISE 104

4. myself; –
5. themselves
6. –
7. each other
8. themselves
9. ourselves (–)
10. herself
11. each other
12. yourself
13. themselves; –
14. yourselves; each other
15. yourself
16. ourselves
17. themselves; each other

EXERCISE 105

A.
2. him
3. their own
4. them
5. their
6. his own
7. his
8. himself
9. his own
10. him
11. mine
12. his
13. his own

B.
1. myself
2. my own
3. myself
4. my own
5. my
6. themselves
7. herself
8. her

Follow-up: Answers will vary.

EXERCISE 106

3. It's (It is) too far.
4. There isn't (There's not; There is not) any cream.
5. It wasn't (was not) nice enough
6. There's (There is) something wrong with it.
7. It's (It is) wonderful
8. There's (There is) a light
9. It's (It is) too late to stop by
10. There isn't (There's not; There is not) enough for everyone.
11. It was very interesting.
12. There was a lot of flu at work last year.
13. There was a lot of snow there last winter.
14. There's (There is) bound to be
15. There used to be

EXERCISE 107

A.
3. somebody
4. anywhere
5. something
6. anybody
7. somebody
8. any
9. somebody
10. Anybody
11. anything

B.
1. anywhere
2. anything
3. anybody
4. somewhere
5. any
6. anybody
7. any

EXERCISE 108

2. 'm (am) not doing anything
3. No one; didn't tell (did not tell) anyone
4. Nowhere; aren't going ('re not going; are not going) anywhere this year
5. None; don't owe (do not owe) me any money
6. Nothing; didn't say (did not say) anything about you
7. Nowhere; don't want (do not want) to go anywhere tomorrow
8. None; doesn't have (does not have) any free time
9. No one; didn't give (did not give) money to anyone
10. Nowhere; didn't put (did not put) your wallet anywhere
11. No one; didn't talk (did not talk) to anyone about your party
12. Nothing; isn't (is not) anything wrong with my car
13. None; haven't gotten any
14. Nothing; wasn't going to say anything

EXERCISE 109

2. none
3. any
4. No
5. any
6. None
7. no
8. nothing
9. nobody
10. any
11. none
12. nobody
13. any
14. no

EXERCISE 110

Corrections are underlined.
3. My brother spends ~~much~~ a lot of time fixing his car.
4. There are plenty of hotels there.
5. She has a few enemies.
6. *RIGHT*
7. Josh has lots of clothes.
8. They go out ~~much~~ a lot.
9. He has a little patience.
10. *RIGHT*
11. There aren't ~~much~~ many reasons to visit that town unless you like old mines.
12. I ate a few hours ago, but I'm hungry again.
13. I haven't gone to the beach on vacation for ~~a lot of~~ many years.
14. *RIGHT*
15. We've gotten plenty of help from friends with our new baby.
16. "A little. What do you need?"
17. There were only a few students who didn't bring their books to class.
18. ~~A lot of~~ Many days, I don't have time to eat lunch.
19. *RIGHT*
20. *RIGHT*
21. *RIGHT*
22. She's gone to Rio a few times, but she doesn't know the city very well.

EXERCISE 111

3. most days
4. both presents
5. both of them
6. either of his brothers
7. either author
8. both days
9. Some days
10. Neither of the presents
11. Some cars
12. some of the money
13. Half of our group (Half our group)
14. Neither of them
15. all the time
16. half of this medicine (half this medicine)

EXERCISE 112

3. Neither of
4. Both of
5. Neither of
6. either of
7. None of; all
8. Neither
9. Neither of; both of
10. All of
11. Both; Either
12. Neither; Both
13. None of
14. all of

EXERCISE 113

3. whole
4. Everyone
5. whole
6. Every
7. Each
8. everyone
9. All
10. everyone
11. all
12. everyone
13. every
14. whole
15. everyone
16. each
17. all
18. all

Follow-up: Answers will vary.

EXERCISE 114

Answers will vary.

EXERCISE 115

4. *RIGHT*
5. who (that) helped him
6. who (that) are moving away
7. who (that) told us to meet him
8. *RIGHT*
9. who (that) was so hospitable
10. that (which) has a social message or that (which) says something
11. that (which) sells photo equipment

12. *RIGHT*
13. *RIGHT*
14. that (which) have good programs
15. *RIGHT*

EXERCISE 116

4. *RIGHT*
5. Where is the restaurant you ate at with friends the other night?
6. Mike applied for a job that was advertised on the Internet.
7. *RIGHT*
8. Good friends are the ones you can rely on.
9. Don't blame me for something someone else did.
10. *RIGHT*
11. *RIGHT*
12. I wonder if you found a pair of glasses I might have left in your café yesterday afternoon.
13. How can I trust someone who lies to me?
14. This store never has anything that fits me right.
15. Phoebe was accepted by the college she was hoping to get into.
16. *RIGHT*

EXERCISE 117

4. b & d
5. b & d
6. a & d
7. b
8. c
9. a & d
10. a & c
11. a
12. a & d
13. b
14. b
15. b & d
16. b & d
17. c
18. a & d

EXERCISE 118

5. why (that) she wants a bigger house
6. that they got married
7. who wanted (wants) to be a soccer player when she grew (grows) up
8. where his wife and daughter both work as police officers
9. why (that); is moving to a new apartment
10. where people get passports
11. whom he sold his car
12. whose anniversary was last week

EXERCISE 119

3. Dolphins, whose brains are slightly larger than human brains, can communicate different kinds of information by making sounds.
4. Americans sometimes compare a foolish or stubborn person to a donkey, which is an animal in the horse family with short legs and long ears.
5. Eagles, whose sharp beaks and very good sight help them hunt, eat small animals.

6. Elephants are protected in many countries, which saves them from being killed for their tusks.
7. Elephants are still being killed by hunters, many of whom hunt illegally.
8. The kangaroo carries its young in its pouch, which is like a big pocket made of skin.
9. The llama, whose wool is soft and expensive, is at home in the Andes Mountains of South America.
10. I have always been fascinated by camels, which are known to travel long distances without water.
11. Many people, most of whom have never seen these animals in the wild, are afraid of rattlesnakes and sharks.
12. Goats, whose reputation for eating anything is well known, live wild in mountain areas or are kept on farms.

EXERCISE 120

1. held; entering
2. won; dominated; called
3. fighting; waiting; winning
4. running; considered

EXERCISE 121

Answers will vary.

EXERCISE 122

3. 's (is) disgusted
4. was depressing
5. was upsetting
6. 's (is) interested
7. were; disappointed
8. 're (are) confusing
9. 're (are) excited
10. was amusing
11. was embarrassed
12. 'll be (will be) freezing
13. were; surprising
14. 'll be (will be) exhausted
15. is shocking
16. won't be bored

EXERCISE 123

2. large green woolen
3. beautiful big old stone
4. typical 16-year-old city
5. big old blue German
6. cute brown and gray Persian
7. favorite traditional Argentine
8. great new Thai
9. blue, yellow, and red (colors may be listed in any order)
10. beautiful old Central Asian
11. nice young foreign
12. modern imported metal
13. delicious aged Italian
14. nice small old
15. good-looking tall blond (tall blond good-looking)

EXERCISE 124

3. incredibly quickly
4. really fluent
5. slowly but carefully

6. very strange for some reason
7. the dress carefully and closely before buying it
8. heavily and continuously for three days
9. seriously injured in the accident
10. surprisingly quickly from her illness
11. cold and incomplete
12. situation; extremely serious
13. incredibly energetic and active
14. hastily and carelessly

EXERCISE 125

A.
5. late
6. hard
7. well
8. fast
9. hardly
10. fast
11. well
12. hardly
13. well
14. good

B.
2. *RIGHT*; *RIGHT*
3. think hard
4. *RIGHT*; late
5. *RIGHT*; well
6. late
7. *RIGHT*; *RIGHT*
8. hard; *RIGHT*
9. *RIGHT*; *RIGHT*
10. well; lately

EXERCISE 126

3. have so much food at home
4. has had such a bad cold
5. was so cold (is so cold)
6. looked so busy
7. 's (is) so old
8. were having such a good time
9. haven't gone (have not gone) for such a long time
10. had so many mistakes
11. didn't live (did not live) so far away
12. live (are living) in such an old house
13. spends so much time
14. to be so nice
15. had such a nice time
16. didn't take so long

EXERCISE 127

A.
2. Mrs. Garcia isn't (is not) healthy enough to live by herself.
3. The jacket was too small for Millie to wear.
4. Josh isn't old enough to drive a car.
5. George is too nice to do such a terrible thing.
6. Do you have enough money to lend me some?
7. I can't type fast enough to finish this report on time.
8. Is there enough water on Mars to support life?
9. Do you know enough German to translate this letter?
10. Is this shirt too big for me?
11. There aren't enough chairs for everyone to sit down.

B.
2. Mrs. Garcia is; to live by herself
3. The jacket wasn't (was not) big enough for Millie to wear.
4. Josh is too young to drive a car.
5. George isn't (is not) mean enough to do such a terrible thing.

EXERCISE 128

3. b
4. b
5. c
6. b
7. a
8. c
9. b
10. a
11. c
12. a
13. b
14. c
15. c
16. c

EXERCISE 129

Answers may vary. Possible answers:
3. more modern
4. cheaper
5. better
6. thinner
7. easier
8. farther
9. earlier
10. larger (bigger)
11. more loudly
12. harder on us (more demanding)
13. safer
14. more carefully
15. friendlier
16. worse
17. more interesting
18. further
19. better
20. prettier (more beautiful)
21. more crowded (worse)
22. worse
23. more quietly
24. better

EXERCISE 130

2. a
3. c
4. c
5. c
6. c
7. c
8. b
9. c
10. a
11. c
12. a
13. c
14. c
15. b

EXERCISE 131

3. more free time than
4. look as well (today) as
5. talk as much as
6. farther to work than
7. to be friendlier than
8. answer the question as intelligently as I expected
9. as many people at the game as usual
10. more comfortable than they look
11. do as well on the test as I'd hoped
12. as much as it did a few years ago
13. to work harder (than she does now)

EXERCISE 132

3. of the busiest people
4. the most dependable friend
5. the oldest child in his family
6. of the most expensive cities in Europe
7. the nicest hotel in the city
8. the most famous person
9. the most pleasant season of the year
10. of the best teams in the country
11. the safest form of transportation
12. of the most difficult questions
13. of the worst students in the class

EXERCISE 133

3. more boring than watching TV
4. less athletic than Frank
5. the most dangerous intersection in
6. happier than (as happy as)
7. are most crowded
8. a more peaceful vacation spot (place) than
9. Ahmed's grade was higher
10. You're funnier than
11. travel farther than Stan
12. better known than Parker Posey
13. the worst experience of
14. A simple solution is often better than

EXERCISE 134

4. the richest person in
5. as badly as
6. harder than
7. more slowly than
8. bigger; the biggest population in
9. as nice as
10. easier; the easiest
11. worse than; as much as
12. as often as; busier than
13. as fast as; longer

EXERCISE 135

2. has probably burned his lunch again
3. almost forgot your birthday last week
4. can only walk with a cane
5. Mrs. Conrad don't usually travel abroad in the winter
6. likes to drink hot chocolate at her desk every morning
7. never has time to go hiking on the weekends
8. like your new suit and overcoat a lot
9. is seldom in her apartment on Saturday
10. forgot your glasses at my house last night
11. will definitely get to work on time next week

12. will also play with his friends in a band on the weekend
13. always says she's sorry, but she usually isn't
14. hardly ever do anything risky

EXERCISE 136

3. isn't (is not) a dry cleaner's anymore
4. are still lots of cars on Main Street
5. don't ride (do not ride) their bikes on Main Street anymore
6. aren't able to go ('re not able to go; are not able to go; can't go; cannot go) to the movies on Main Street anymore
7. don't have trouble parking downtown anymore
8. can still find something to read in town
9. 's (is) not hard to find a place to eat on Main Street
10. are still trees along Main Street
11. can't get (cannot get) a suit or dress dry-cleaned on Main Street anymore

EXERCISE 137

2. even
3. even though
4. even
5. Even though
6. even
7. even
8. even if (if)
9. if
10. even
11. if
12. even
13. even though
14. If

Follow-up: Answers will vary.

EXERCISE 138

Added words are underlined.
2. I <u>still</u> can't find Sally's address <u>on my laptop</u>.
3. Maybe we don't <u>even</u> have the address <u>anymore</u>.
4. I <u>sometimes</u> drink a glass of milk <u>before bed</u>. (<u>Sometimes</u>, I drink a glass of milk <u>before bed</u>.)
5. I <u>never</u> drink coffee <u>at home after 3 p.m.</u>
6. Are you and <u>all</u> your brothers at home <u>tonight</u>? (Are you and your brothers <u>all</u> at home <u>tonight</u>?)
7. Sheila <u>almost</u> fell off a ladder <u>at work yesterday</u>. (<u>Yesterday</u>, Sheila <u>almost</u> fell off a ladder <u>at work</u>.)
8. Have you and Sam <u>both</u> voted <u>yet</u>? (Have <u>both</u> you and Sam voted <u>yet</u>?)
9. Kim <u>probably</u> won't be at work <u>tomorrow</u>.
10. My children are <u>hardly ever</u> late <u>for dinner</u>.
11. <u>Even</u> a child can <u>easily</u> understand this poem.
12. Have you <u>already</u> taken out the garbage <u>today</u>?
13. We have <u>not</u> heard from Ken <u>in Miami yet</u>.
14. Can you <u>still</u> give me a ride <u>home after work</u>?
15. Bill and Sue are <u>probably no longer</u> working <u>at the bank</u>.
16. I want you <u>both</u> to stop arguing <u>right now</u>.
17. Stan and Ted <u>both</u> moved <u>to Houston last month</u>. (<u>Both</u> Stan and Ted moved <u>to Houston last month</u>.)
18. Sally has <u>always</u> gotten to work <u>on time</u>.
19. Are your parents <u>still</u> in town, or have they <u>already</u> gone back home? (Are your parents <u>still</u> in town, or have they gone back home <u>already</u>?)

20. I can't remember his name <u>anymore</u>, but I can <u>still</u> picture his face.
21. Did they <u>definitely</u> say to meet them <u>at the club at 5:30</u>?
22. This computer was <u>even</u> cheaper <u>last week</u> <u>at another store</u>.

EXERCISE 139

Answers will vary.

EXERCISE 140

2. really sick, my sister had to take care of my nephew
3. I didn't care (did not care) for the lunch my aunt made, I ate it anyway
4. I wasn't (was not) very busy yesterday. I forgot to go to the bank
5. my sister had a flu shot, she still got the flu
6. answer, Angela didn't (did not) show any anger herself
7. I didn't have much money as a student, I managed to graduate by working part-time
8. I wasn't (was not) very hungry. I went to a restaurant with my friends
9. having problems with her teenagers; manages to stay in a good mood
10. she (Sandy) wanted to visit Mongolia, Sandy (she) only went to Beijing
11. it was a beautiful day, I stayed inside to study
12. having money problems, Cal bought a new shirt

EXERCISE 141

3. You should take extra money along on your trip; you need it in San Francisco
4. The Suarez teenagers can stay out late; they call home to say where they are
5. go running in the morning; it's raining
6. Ted always leaves his phone number with the babysitter; she needs to contact him
7. will get along with Angela; you're careful what you say to her
8. I can go to the movies with you; (that) you pay for my ticket
9. don't you take your allergy medicine along; you need it
10. My computer printer usually works well; I haven't been using it too much
11. (that) I have enough money; go to Hawaii with you
12. I'm going to lend Tom the car; you need it
13. went to the party a little early; the hostess needed some help
14. you think you'll eat them; going to take these leftovers home

EXERCISE 142

Corrections are underlined.
3. Most U.S. students are 18 <u>when</u> they graduate from high school.
4. <u>As</u> you may have heard, Richard is now the director of his company.
5. *RIGHT*
6. *RIGHT*
7. A lot of players get injured in sports <u>like</u> hockey and football.
8. <u>Like</u> her coworkers, Pam has to pay for her own uniforms since the company doesn't provide them.

9. Don't tie the package that way. I'll show you – do it <u>like</u> this.
10. Selma works <u>as</u> a nurse, but she was trained to be a doctor in her country.
11. As usual, Tim spent his weekend on his hobbies, things <u>like</u> gardening and painting.
12. Since we're all hungry, let's sit down and eat. Sue can eat <u>when</u> she gets here.
13. My feet are really cold. They feel <u>like</u> ice.
14. *RIGHT* (The party didn't turn out <u>as</u> I expected, but it was a lot of fun anyway.)
15. *RIGHT*

EXERCISE 143

2. g
3. a
4. h
5. b
6. f
7. c
8. e

Follow-up: Answers will vary.

EXERCISE 144

2. As
3. as if
4. as
5. As
6. when
7. As
8. like
9. Since
10. like
11. as
12. as though
13. as if
14. like
15. as
16. like
17. as if
18. When
19. as though
20. as if
21. as
22. as
23. Like
24. as if
25. like

EXERCISE 145

2. for
3. While
4. for
5. for
6. while
7. until
8. for
9. until
10. during
11. by the time
12. while
13. until
14. by

15. until
16. by
17. By the time
18. until
19. during
20. while

EXERCISE 146

Answers will vary.

EXERCISE 147

1. b. on (–)
   c. at; at
   d. In
2. a. in
   b. –
   c. on
3. a. at; at
   b. in; in; at
   c. –
4. a. in
   b. in
   c. at
   d. In
   e. in
5. a. on
   b. in
   c. in
6. a. At; in
   b. at
   c. in
7. a. at
   b. in
   c. in

EXERCISE 148

2. in; at
3. at; at
4. in (at)
5. at; on
6. at; in; on
7. at; at
8. at; on
9. in; in
10. on
11. in; at
12. in
13. on; on
14. on; in
15. on; on
16. in
17. on
18. on; in
19. at; at
20. on; in (at)
21. in
22. on

EXERCISE 149

2. into; at; in
3. on; on; to
4. on; on
5. to; on

6. –; to
7. on; to
8. in; in; In
9. –; to
10. on; on
11. in; on
12. at
13. in; –; in

EXERCISE 150

2. by; on
3. on; in
4. with; by
5. by; on
6. with; in; to
7. by; by
8. on
9. in; by
10. by; with
11. on; on; by
12. by; by; by
13. by; In; by
14. on; On; by
15. to; on; in
16. by; for; on

EXERCISE 151

Answers will vary.

EXERCISE 152

Answers will vary.

EXERCISE 153

3. The damage to many buildings is extensive.
4. The cause of the argument isn't (is not) clear to me.
5. There's (There is) an urgent need for blankets and clothes.
6. It isn't (is not) easy to find a solution to that problem.
7. I didn't know (did not know) the answer to that question.
8. His relationship with his father isn't (is not) very good.
9. It is hard to tell the difference between them.
10. The advantage of a laptop is its portability.

EXERCISE 154

4. Are you; by the price of gas
5. was; of you to give your brother the last piece of cake
6. Are you; by Max's progress in English
7. Linda is; by school
8. I'm (I am); by his knowledge of insects
9. were; with the service at the restaurant
10. I'm (I am); at Jerry for forgetting to invite me to his party
11. Are you; with my solution to the problem
12. Everyone was; with the little girl's song
13. was; of George to spend all his money on a new shirt
14. was; of Sally to shake hands with everyone in the room

EXERCISE 155

2. ashamed of
3. jealous of
4. sure of
5. responsible for

6. tired of
7. aware of
8. capable of
9. worried about
10. different from (than)
11. short of
12. tolerant of
13. suspicious of
14. similar to
15. proud of
16. married to; engaged to

EXERCISE 156

2. shouted at
3. talk to
4. describe to
5. explain to
6. throw; to
7. apologized to; for
8. thank; for
9. explain; to
10. Ask
11. aim at
12. laughing at
13. answer
14. point; at
15. staring at
16. glance at; call

EXERCISE 157

2. for her
3. of them
4. about it
5. for them
6. about it
7. about it
8. for it
9. about them
10. for them
11. for them
12. for it
13. for him
14. to them
15. after him
16. for her
17. about it
18. for it
19. of him; after him
20. for them

EXERCISE 158

2. me of someone I know
3. Amy complained; for her new car
4. from Hannah since last summer
5. from heart disease; from
6. of (about) moving to San Francisco
7. me of being lazy
8. That child; on cereal and milk
9. This sunscreen; from
10. people about (of) serious weather conditions
11. of the name of that restaurant
12. me for your

13. on how much
14. me on
15. of Pablo Neruda

EXERCISE 159

2. b
3. a
4. b
5. a
6. c
7. c
8. a
9. c
10. c
11. a
12. c
13. c
14. b
15. c
16. c

EXERCISE 160

Answers will vary.

EXERCISE 161

Answers may vary. Possible answers:
2. c; e
3. a; b
4. a; b; c
5. a

EXERCISE 162

2. walked out of
3. eat out
4. fit in
5. plug; in
6. dropped out of
7. letting; in
8. joined in
9. fill out
10. get out of
11. go into
12. drop in
13. leave out
14. moved in
15. locked; out
16. check out of

EXERCISE 163

2. find out
3. turned out
4. pointing out
5. worked out
6. put; out
7. handing out
8. try out
9. put out
10. worked; out
11. run out
12. gone out
13. working out

14. blow; out
15. carrying out
16. figure out

EXERCISE 164

2. drop
3. rip
4. laid
5. try
6. putting
7. taking
8. have
9. go
10. called
11. put
12. see
13. doze
14. went
15. going
16. take
17. get
18. Turn
19. Hold

EXERCISE 165

Answers will vary.

EXERCISE 166

2. cut down
3. taken down
4. put up
5. been picked up
6. slow down
7. writing down
8. broke down
9. cut down
10. let down
11. turned down
12. burn down
13. close; down

EXERCISE 167

2. ended up
3. grew up
4. brought up
5. keep up
6. gave up
7. catch up
8. backed up
9. show up
10. back up
11. walked up
12. end up
13. takes up
14. gave up
15. made up

EXERCISE 168

Corrections are underlined.

2. The enemy blew up the bridge into town.
3. How can you put up with such rude behavior?
4. We were held up by an accident on the highway.
5. Rose and her husband are splitting up after 20 years of marriage.
6. Phil and Sue are saving up to buy a car.
7. When you talk to the boss, never bring up our salaries.
8. That little boy was beaten up by older boys at the school.
9. She made up the whole thing.
10. We couldn't play our match until it cleared up.
11. My brother and I look a lot alike. People are always mixing us up.
12. He always comes up with something useful to say.

EXERCISE 169

Answers may vary. Possible answers:

2. b; c
3. a
4. c; d
5. b
6. a

EXERCISE 170

Answers will vary.

ILLUSTRATION CREDIT

All illustrations by Randy Jones and Susann Ferris Jones

PHOTO CREDITS